# THE LITTLE HOUSE

## STORY AND PICTURES
### BY
### VIRGINIA LEE BURTON

HOUGHTON MIFFLIN COMPANY · BOSTON

To

Dorgie

Once upon a time
there was a Little House
way out in the country.
She was a pretty Little House
and she was strong and well built.
The man who built her so well said,
"This Little House shall never be sold
for gold or silver and she will live to see
our great-great-grandchildren's
great-great-grandchildren living in her."

1

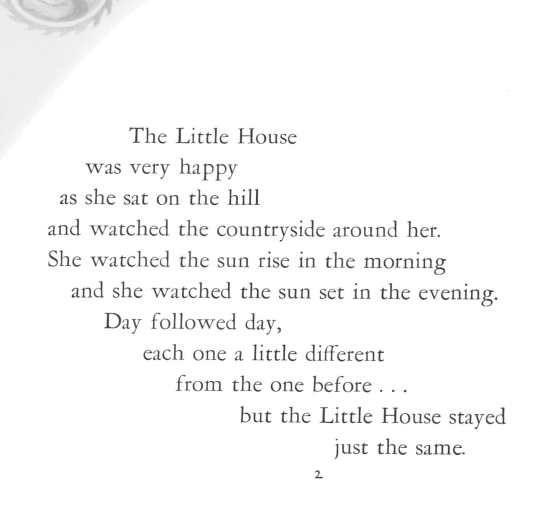

The Little House
was very happy
as she sat on the hill
and watched the countryside around her.
She watched the sun rise in the morning
and she watched the sun set in the evening.
Day followed day,
each one a little different
from the one before . . .
but the Little House stayed
just the same.

2

In the nights
she watched the moon grow
from a thin new moon to a full moon,
then back again to a thin old moon;
and when there was no moon
she watched the stars.
Way off in the distance
she could see the lights of the city.
The Little House was curious about the city
and wondered what it would be like to live there.

4

Time passed quickly
for the Little House
as she watched the countryside
slowly change with the seasons.
In the Spring,
when the days grew longer
and the sun warmer,
she waited for the first robin
to return from the South.
She watched the grass turn green.
She watched the buds on the trees swell
and the apple trees burst into blossom.
She watched the children
playing in the brook.

6

In the long Summer days
she sat in the sun
and watched the trees
cover themselves with leaves
and the white daisies cover the hill.
She watched the gardens grow,
and she watched the apples turn red and ripen.
She watched the children swimming in the po

8

In the Fall,
  when the days grew shorter
and the nights colder,
  she watched the first frost
    turn the leaves to bright yellow
      and orange and red.
          She watched the harvest gathered
            and the apples picked.
                She watched the children
                    going back to school.

In the Winter,
   when the nights were long and the days short,
  and the countryside covered with snow,
she watched the children
coasting and skating.
  Year followed year. . . .
    The apple trees grew old
      and new ones were planted.
       The children grew up
        and went away to the city . . .
         and now at night
          the lights of the city
           seemed brighter and closer.

12

One day
the Little House
was surprised to see
a horseless carriage coming down
the winding country road. . . .
Pretty soon there were more of them
on the road and fewer carriages pulled by horses.
Pretty soon along came some surveyors and surveyed a line
in front of the Little House.
Pretty soon along came a steam shovel and dug a road
through the hill covered with daisies. . . .
Then some trucks came and dumped big stones on the road,
then some trucks with little stones,
then some trucks with tar and sand,
and finally a steam roller came
and rolled it all smooth,
and the road was done.

14

Now the Little House
watched the trucks and automobiles
going back and forth to the city.
Gasoline stations . . .
roadside stands . . .
and small houses
followed the new road.
Everyone and everything
moved much faster now than before.

More roads were made,
and the countryside was divided into lots.
More houses and bigger houses . . .
apartment houses and tenement houses . . .
schools . . . stores . . . and garages
spread over the land
and crowded around the Little House.
No one wanted to live in her
and take care of her any more.
She couldn't be sold for gold or silver,
so she just stayed there and watched.

18

Now it was not so quiet and peaceful at night.
Now the lights of the city were bright and very close,
and the street lights shone all night.
"This must be living in the city,"
thought the Little House,
and didn't know whether she liked it or not.
She missed the field of daisies
and the apple trees dancing in the moonlight.

20

Pretty soon
there were trolley cars
going back and forth
in front of the Little House.
They went back and forth
all day and part of the night.
Everyone seemed to be very busy
and everyone seemed to be in a hurry.

22

Pretty soon there was an elevated train
going back and forth above the Little House.
The air was filled with dust and smoke,
and the noise was so loud
that it shook the Little House.
Now she couldn't tell when Spring came,
or Summer or Fall, or Winter.
It all seemed about the same.

24

Pretty soon
there was a subway
going back and forth
underneath the Little House.
She couldn't see it,
but she could feel and hear it.
People were moving faster and faster.
No one noticed the Little House any more.
They hurried by without a glance.

26

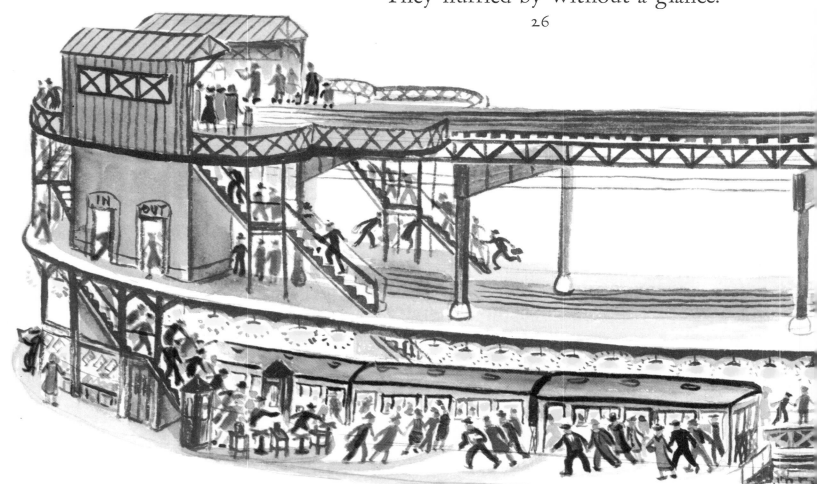

Pretty soon they tore down
the apartment houses and tenement houses
around the Little House
and started digging big cellars . . . one on each side.
The steam shovels dug down three stories on one side
and four stories on the other side.
Pretty soon they started building up . . .
They built up twenty-five stories on one side
and thirty-five stories on the other.

28

Now the Little House only saw the sun at noon,
and didn't see the moon or stars at night at all
because the lights of the city were too bright.
She didn't like living in the city.
At night she used to dream of the country
and the field of daisies
and the apple trees
dancing in the moonlight.

30

The Little House
was very sad and lonely.
Her paint was cracked and dirty . . .
Her windows were broken and her shutters hung crookedly.
She looked shabby . . . though she was just as good a house as ever underneath.

Then one fine morning in Spring
along came the great-great-granddaughter
of the man who built the Little House so well.
She saw the shabby Little House, but she didn't hurry by
There was something about the Little House
that made her stop and look again.
She said to her husband,
"That Little House looks just like the Little House
my grandmother lived in when she was a little girl,
only *that* Little House was way out in the country
on a hill covered with daisies
and apple trees growing around."

They found out it was the very same house,
so they went to the Movers to see
if the Little House could be moved.
The Movers looked the Little House all over
and said, "Sure, this house is as good as ever.
She's built so well we could move her anywhere."
So they jacked up the Little House
and put her on wheels.
Traffic was held up for hours
as they slowly moved her
out of the city.

At first
the Little House
was frightened,
but after she got used to it
she rather liked it.
They rolled along the big road,
and they rolled along the little roads,
until they were way out in the country.
When the Little House saw the green grass
and heard the birds singing, she didn't feel sad any more.
They went along and along, but they couldn't seem to find
just the right place.
They tried the Little House here,
and they tried her there.
Finally they saw a little hill
in the middle of a field . . .
and apple trees growing around.
"There," said the great-great-granddaughter,
"that's just the place."
"Yes, it is," said the Little House to herself.
A cellar was dug on top of the hill
and slowly they moved the house
from the road to the hill.

37

The windows and shutters were fixed
and once again they painted her
a lovely shade of pink.
As the Little House settled down
on her new foundation,
she smiled happily.
Once again she could watch
the sun and moon and stars.
Once again she could watch
Spring and Summer
and Fall and Winter
come and g

38

Once again
    she was lived in
        and taken care of.

Never again would she be curious about the city . . .
Never again would she want to live there . . .
The stars twinkled above her . . .
A new moon was coming up . . .
It was Spring . . .
and all was quiet and peaceful in the country.

HILLTOP ELEMENTARY SCHOOL

# PART THREE

# HIGH SCHOOL INQUIRIES

# CHAPTER 12

# Teaching about Korea in the **High School**

Kathy Swan, John Lee, and S.G. Grant

As might be expected, the typical high school social studies program offers the most opportunities to use the inquiries in this book. Those opportunities include prospects for both broad coverage and in-depth study of topics that focus on either a single discipline (e.g., economics, history) or on a multi-disciplinary approach. As with the inquiries in the previous sections, these high school inquiries reflect both past and present circumstances, though there is considerably more attention to contemporary life than in the earlier sections. The Korean War remains a defining event in both Korean and United States history. But it is how these nations move forward that matters.

Although the social studies curriculum in high schools exhibits some patterns, it does so within a considerable range of diversity.[1] The patterns lie mainly in the 11th and 12th grade years. Standard practice calls for a United States history course in eleventh grade and a government or civics course in twelfth. The former is typically a year-long survey that begins either with early explorations or with the settling of the American colonies by the British. In twelfth grade, the study of U.S. politics is common, though the focus may differ from state to state. Many senior courses, of either a half-year or full-year duration, examine the structures of government, the role of politics, and the duties of active citizenship. Others, however, assume that these matters have been taught at earlier grades and so the curricular emphasis is on contemporary issues—e.g., the death penalty, gun control, federalism, and voting rights.

Considerably more diversity in the high school curriculum typically appears in the 9th and 10th grades. Many states use one or both of these years to teach world history. For example, New York State requires a two-year course in global history and geography in ninth and tenth grade. By contrast, California requires a single year of modern world history in tenth grade, but offers a range of elective social science-based courses in ninth grade.

The curriculum similarities and differences across the United States aside, the point is clear: Teachers interested in using the Korea-based inquiries in this book (or those of their own creation) should face no insurmountable curricular challenge. They will face the ever-present constraint of teaching time, but they will find plenty of material and guidance in these inquiries to enhance their current instructional efforts.

---

In the section that follows, we briefly describe each of the curriculum inquiries written with high school students in mind.

The set of inquiries begins with one that focuses on a contemporary economics issue—the impact of conglomerates. The South Korean version of this institution (chaebol) has features that distinguish it from its U.S. equivalent (e.g., chaebols tend to be run by individual families whereas U.S.-based conglomerates are typically own jointly by stockholders). That said, the two forms are far more common than different (e.g., the accumulation of similar and diverse financial assets).[2]

The compelling question for Chapter 13 is "Are Conglomerates Good for the Economy?" The question asks students to consider the benefits and drawbacks of chaebols in a case study of the conglomerate phenomena and then make a determination as to their value. In their evidence-based arguments, students can draw from a wide range of primary and secondary sources including the documentary film, "The Legacy," produced by the Korean War Legacy Project (KWLP).

In Chapter 14, students take on the question: Why Was the Korean War "Forgotten"? Given the role that the war played in the U.S.-Communist tensions of the time and the subsequent birth of an economic and democratic dynamo in South Korea, it is challenging to think that this event could be forgotten.[3] And yet even a quick survey of most state curriculums reveals little explicit mention of Korea either in historical or contemporary terms.

The inquiry in Chapter 14 should go some distance to correcting that omission, at least in terms of the Korean War itself. Students examine the escalation from a conflict to a war and how and why Americans ignored the developing situation. Then, using archived KWLP interviews and their school textbooks, students explore the idea of how an historical event can be forgotten.

Chapter 15 ("What Has Korea Meant to the United States?") traces the evolution of the relationship between South Korea and the United States from the 1950s on. Drawing on a rich array of primary and secondary sources, students should have all that they need to examine each phase of the transition from the U.S. occupation of Korea to the post-war development of close and enduring political, economic, and diplomatic ties.

In what might be considered a companion piece, Chapter 16 focuses students' attention on the evolving relationship between the United States and North Korea. Continuing the themes of the importance of words and media developed in the middle school inquiries, the compelling question behind this chapter—"How Should We Talk with North Korea?"— positions students to see how personalities, events, and circumstances and the words used to describe them change over time.

To reinforce the dynamic quality of international relations, the final supporting question asks students to seek out current sources on the ongoing relationship between the North Korean and United States governments. The inquiries in this section are richly sourced. Charting how students read and interpret those sources offers teachers important insights into their students' disciplinary thinking. But teachers will also want to see if students can apply that thinking in the search for additional sources.[4]

As in the previous sections, we pause here to highlight some of the notable features inherent in this set of inquiries.

More so than in the previous sections, the high school-level inquiries demonstrate the importance of students being able to see the threads of the past emerge in contemporary situations. The last two chapters illustrate this point explicitly, but students and their teachers can also see how events in the past have shaped the questions around issues like the emergence of conglomerates and the changing image of the Korean War.

Showing students how the past connects with the present is one way to ensure that an inquiry meets the criteria both of academic rigor and student relevance for a compelling question. But the four high school inquiries also offer strong content and appeal to students in other ways. One is the idea of something being "forgotten." Despite having lived a relatively short time, secondary-level students have had sufficient lived experience to appreciate how and why some things are remembered and others overlooked. By high school, students have also experienced a range of relationships. Drawing on those relationships, students can appreciate and understand the complexity, the vagaries, and the uncertainties that can surface when the leaders of countries interact with one another.

Connecting the content of an inquiry to students' lives is important. One of the keys to doing that, however, is the kind of sources that students encounter. Many readers will remember their own high school social studies courses and the dominance of a single source—a mass-produced textbook. Those textbooks can be useful, but only if students have access to the rich primary and secondary sources available. The range of sources included in the high school inquiries do two things. First, they richly enhance the pedagogical power of the inquiries at hand by offering more substance and a greater number of different perspectives than textbooks can provide. Second, the featured sources signal to teachers just how wide the source possibilities are. Seeing their students embrace these different avenues is likely to inspire teachers to pump up their source use in other curriculum units that they teach.

One final feature of the high school inquiries emerges when teachers see a mix of longer and shorter approaches to building an inquiry-based practice. Teaching through inquiry can take more instructional time than more didactic methods, but it need not. Teachers who transform their current curriculum units into full inquiries may find that the depth of study required takes more classroom time to achieve. But the "Conglomerate" inquiry (like the "Media" and "Sacrifice" inquiries in the middle school section) demonstrates that teachers can build an authentic inquiry experience into a relatively short span of time. The Inquiry Design Model is based on the assumption that teachers are knowledgeable about their content and pedagogy and that they want to push themselves and their students to deeper and richer understandings.[5] If doing so through inquiry makes them nervous, then the more focused and time-sensitive inquiries could be their entry points.

Although creating space for their students to study Korea in both past and present conditions may be easier for high school teachers than for their peers in the earlier grades, the challenges of too much content and too little instructional time remain. To that end, the inquiries in this section represent a "good" problem. The good part is the rich pedagogical possibilities that these inquiries embody; each one positions students to delve deeply into a topic and a compelling question about that topic that honor their experiences in and their curiosity about the world around them. The problem is the tyranny of time; the school year is simply not long enough for all the good work teachers and their students can do.

So teachers are constantly faced with thorny decisions around where to spend their and their students' instructional lives. Developing an inquiry-based practice will not eliminate teachers' need to make hard decisions. But seeing their students embrace the questions, tasks, and sources in front of them will make them smile.

**NOTES**

1.   E. W. Ross, *The Social Studies Curriculum: Purposes, Problems, and Possibilities*, 3rd ed. (Albany, NY: SUNY Press, 2006); S. Thornton, *Teaching Social Studies that Matters: Curriculum for Active Learning* (New York: Teachers College Press, 2004).

2.   C. Tejada, "Money, Power, Family: Inside South Korea's Chaebol," *The New York Times*, February 17, 2017.

3.   S. Casey, *Selling the Korean War: Propaganda, Politics, and Public Opinion in the United States, 1950-1953* (Oxford, UK: Oxford University Press, 2010); B. Cumings, *The Korean War: A History* (New York: Modern Library, 2011); M. Pash, *In the Shadow of the Greatest Generation: The Americans who fought the Korean War* (New York: NYU Press, 2014).

4.   S. G. Grant, K. Swan, and J. Lee, *Inquiry-based Practice in Social Studies Education* (New York: Routledge, 2017).

5.   S. G. Grant, K. Swan, and J. Lee, *op. cit.*

# Are Conglomerates **Good for the Economy**?

Thomas Clouse and Kathy Swan

Busan at night.
GETTY IMAGES

# ARE CONGLOMERATES GOOD FOR THE ECONOMY?

| | |
|---|---|
| **C3 Framework Indicator** | **D2.Eco.15.9-12**. Explain how current globalization trends and policies affect economic growth, labor markets, rights of citizens, the environment, and resource and income distribution in different nations. |
| **Staging the Compelling Question** | Examine a set of economic datagraphics and create a claim about the economic health of the Republic of Korea. |

| SUPPORTING QUESTION 1 | SUPPORTING QUESTION 2 |
|---|---|
| What is a chaebol? | What are the benefits and drawbacks of chaebols? |
| **FORMATIVE PERFORMANCE TASK** | **FORMATIVE PERFORMANCE TASK** |
| Write a definition of a chaebol and describe its significance to the Korean economy. | Create a graphic organizer showing evidence of the benefits and drawbacks of the chaebol system. |
| **FEATURED SOURCES** | **FEATURED SOURCES** |
| **Source A:** Excerpt from an article, "Money, Power, Family: Inside South Korea's Chaebol," *The New York Times,* February 17, 2017<br>**Source B:** Bar graph showing the economic weight of chaebols in the South Korean economy, using data from the Korea Fair Trade Commission | **Source A:** Video, "How Samsung Dominates South Korea's Economy," CNN, February 17, 2017<br>**Source B:** Timeline, "South Korea's Conglomerates," *Sage Business Researcher,* August 21, 2017<br>**Source C:** Article on "The Death of Daewoo," *The Economist,* August 19, 1999<br>**Source D:** Article, "South Korea's Moon Vows to Rev Up Jobs and Rein in 'Chaebol,'" *Nikkei Asian Review,* May 18, 2017<br>**Source E:** Documentary film, "The Legacy," Korean War Legacy Project, 2018 |

| | |
|---|---|
| **Summative Performance Task** | **ARGUMENT** Are conglomerates good for the economy? Use evidence to construct a claim and a counterclaim that address the compelling question. |
| | **EXTENSION** Use gapminder.org to research the impact of South Korea's economic boom on its society, health, environment, education, and infrastructure in order to revise or strengthen your argument. |

## Overview
### Inquiry Description

The compelling question for this inquiry calls on students to consider whether conglomerates are good for the economy. Specifically, this focused inquiry is a case study of South Korean conglomerations, known as *chaebol* or *chaebols*. After the Korean War, large sums of money were given to a handful of corporations (for example, Samsung, Lotte, Hyundai, and Daewoo) in order to spur economic growth in the South. The chaebols, including Samsung, Hyundai, and Daewoo, would play an important role in spurring economic growth by focusing on the export of cheap electronic goods. At the same time, these chaebols were protected by the government because of the belief that they were "too big to fail." Currently, corrupt business practices by chaebol leaders have led some Koreans to question whether or not chaebols should be dismantled. In this focused inquiry, students will work with a variety of sources in order to answer whether or not such conglomerates or chaebols are good for the economy. Although the focus of this inquiry is on Korean conglomerates, this examination has students wrestle with the idea of how countries should develop economically.

This inquiry is expected to take four to seven 55-minute class periods. The inquiry time frame could expand if teachers think their students need additional instructional experiences (i.e., supporting questions, formative tasks, and sources). Inquiries are not scripts, and teachers are encouraged to modify and adapt them in order to meet the requirements and interests of their particular students. Resources can also be modified as necessary to meet individualized education programs (IEPs) or Section 504 plans for students with disabilities.

## Structure of the Inquiry

In addressing the compelling question "Are conglomerates good for the economy?" students will work through two supporting questions, formative performance tasks, and a number of sources in order to construct a claim and counterclaim supported by evidence.

### STAGING THE COMPELLING QUESTION

The inquiry begins with students examining four documents highlighting the economic situation in the Republic of Korea. The first document is a line graph illustrating World Bank data on how the Republic of Korea's Gross Domestic Product (GDP) has changed since 1960. Teachers will want students to be able to recognize that generally GDP has greatly increased, but students should also consider possible causes of dips in progress along the way.

The second document is a list of countries ranked by GDP. Teachers will want to point out the Republic of Korea's position on the list, noting also those nations ranking higher and lower than South Korea.

The third source is a table of income inequality (Gini coefficient) and poverty (relative poverty) for select countries. Teachers will want to ensure students understand both measures. The Gini coefficient measures the economic equality within a country: a score of "0" means a country has perfect economic equality; a score of "1" means the country has perfect economic inequality (i.e., one person has all the wealth). Relative poverty measures the percentage of people whose income is less than half of the national median income.

The final source is a bar graph illustrating how much of the wealth in South Korea is controlled by the top 10 percent of the population, and how that compares with other countries in the region.

From these documents, students should be able to discuss whether or not they believe the economy of the Republic of Korea to be economically healthy.

## SUPPORTING QUESTION 1

The first supporting question—"What is a chaebol?" —is a foundational question when examining the South Korean economy. The formative performance task asks students to write a definition of a chaebol and describe its significance to the South Korean economy using the sources provided. Featured Source A is an excerpt from the *New York Times* article, "Money, Power, Family: Inside South Korea's Chaebol." This article defines the term "chaebol" and details how the conglomerates have become integrated into the political sphere in South Korea. Featured Source B is a bar graph showing the economic weight of chaebols in South Korea's economy. Teachers may want to draw parallels between conglomerates in the United States and chaebols in South Korea.

## SUPPORTING QUESTION 2

The second supporting question—"What are the benefits and drawbacks of chaebols?"— helps students synthesize both sides of the chaebol debate. The formative performance task calls on students to create a graphic organizer in which they record evidence highlighting either the benefits or the drawbacks of the chaebols for the overall economy. Featured Source A is a short CNN video, "How Samsung Dominates South Korea's Economy." It provides a brief look at the diversity of products and interests that are housed under the Samsung name. Featured Source B is a timeline tracing South Korea's economic rise with the rise of the chaebols and democracy. The timeline comes from the article "South Korea's Conglomerates," from *Sage Business Researcher*. While Featured Sources A and B define chaebols and put them in context in South Korea's modern history, Featured Source C looks at what happens when a chaebol fails. This article from the *Economist*, "The Death of Daewoo," examines not only why the chaebol failed, but also the real and imagined impact of its failure on the Korean economy. Teachers will want students to think about whether or not these chaebols are really "too big to fail." Featured Source D is an article from the *Nikkei Asian Review* in May 2017, "South Korea's Moon Vows to Rev Up Jobs and Rein in 'Chaebol'." The article examines how South Korea's new president, Moon Jae-in, will attempt to limit the power of the chaebol and instead focus on small and medium size businesses for capital investment. Featured Source E is a clip from "The Legacy," a documentary from the Korean War Legacy Project. Minutes 23:05 to 25:55 of the video feature Dr. Jongwoo Han explaining the rise of the South Korean economy after the Korean War.

## SUMMATIVE PERFORMANCE TASK

In this task, students construct an evidence-based argument responding to the prompt, "Are conglomerates good for the economy?" Teachers will want to have students refer back to the graphic organizer they filled out in the inquiry as a way to focus their responses. In this focused inquiry, students are asked to develop a claim and counterclaim with evidence from the sources they examined during the inquiry. Students' arguments will vary, but could include any of the following:

- Conglomerates are good for the economy. Using the Republic of Korea as an example, conglomerates known as chaebols helped bring about the "economic miracle" in the Republic of Korea and continue to be a large contributor to the economic health of the country.

- Conglomerates are not good for the economy. Using the Republic of Korea as an example, conglomerates known as chaebols have been propped up as "too big to fail" and have been found to foster widespread, corrupt business practices and eliminate the growth of smaller companies.

- Conglomerates are both good and bad for the economy. Using the Republic of Korea as an example, conglomerates known as chaebols helped to spur the "economic miracle" in the Republic of Korea, but have also fostered corrupt business practices and halted innovation by smaller companies.

- Students could extend these arguments by using Gapminder.org to research the impact of the economic boom on South Korea's society, health, environment, education, and infrastructure.

## Staging the Compelling Question

**FEATURED SOURCE** Line graph of South Korea's Gross Domestic Product (GDP) per capita from 1960 to the present, according to World Bank data, excerpted from Kim Jaewon, "South Korea's Moon Vows to Rev Up Jobs and Rein in 'Chaebol,'" *Nikkei Asian Review*, May 18, 2017.

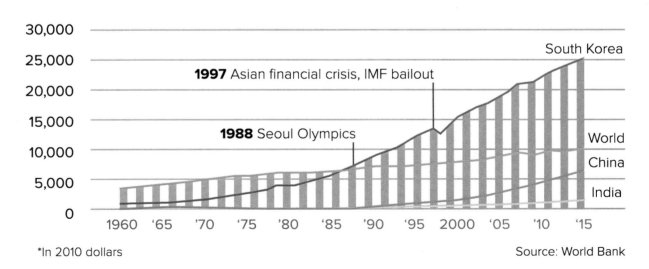

South Korea's Economic Success
(GDP PER CAPITA, INFLATION-ADJUSTED*)

*In 2010 dollars

Source: World Bank

# Staging the Compelling Question

**FEATURED SOURCE** Rankings of countries by Gross Domestic Product, 2016, World Bank.

| Ranking | Economy | (millions of dollars) |
|---|---|---|
| 1 | United States | 19,485,394 |
| 2 | China | 12,237,700 |
| 3 | Japan | 4,872,415 |
| 4 | Germany | 3,693,204 |
| 5 | India | 2,650,725 |
| 6 | United Kingdom | 2,637,866 |
| 7 | France | 2,582,501 |
| 8 | Brazil | 2,053,595 |
| 9 | Italy | 1,943,835 |
| 10 | Canada | 1,647,120 |
| 11 | Russian Federation | 1,578,417 |
| 12 | Republic of Korea | 1,530,751 |
| 13 | Australia | 1,323,421 |
| 14 | Spain | 1,314,314 |
| 15 | Mexico | 1,150,888 |
| 16 | Indonesia | 1,015,421 |
| 17 | Turkey | 851,549 |
| 18 | Netherlands | 830,573 |
| 19 | Saudi Arabia | 686,738 |
| 20 | Switzerland | 678,965 |
| 21 | Argentina | 637,430 |
| 22 | Sweden | 535,607 |
| 23 | Poland | 526,466 |
| 24 | Belgium | 494,764 |
| 25 | Thailand | 455,303 |

SOURCE: HTTP://DATABANK.WORLDBANK.ORG/DATA/DOWNLOAD/GDP.PDF
PUBLISHED UNDER CREATIVE COMMONS 4.0

## Staging the Compelling Question

**FEATURED SOURCE** Income distribution and relative poverty in selected countries, Organization for Economic Co-operation and Development (OECD), 2015.

| Country | Gini Coefficient | Relative Poverty (2015) |
| --- | --- | --- |
| Republic of Korea | 0.295 | 13.8% |
| United States | 0.39 | 16.8% |
| Canada | 0.313 | 12.6% |
| Japan | 0.33 | 16.1% |
| Italy | 0.326 | 13.7% |
| France | 0.297 | 8.2% |
| Mexico | 0.459 | 10.4% |

SOURCE: OECD, HTTP://WWW.OECD.ORG/SOCIAL/INEQUALITY.HTM

## Staging the Compelling Question

**FEATURED SOURCE** Bar graph illustrating the percentage of total income earned by the wealthiest 10% of the total population, by country. excerpted from Kim Kyung-rok, "Income Inequality in South Korea the Most Severe in Asia," *Hankyoreh*, March 17, 2016.

http://english.hani.co.kr/arti/english_edition/e_national/735462.html

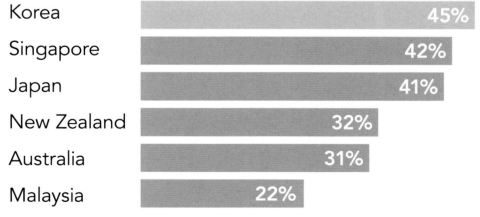

### Percentage of Total Income Earned by the Top 10%

| | |
| --- | --- |
| Korea | 45% |
| Singapore | 42% |
| Japan | 41% |
| New Zealand | 32% |
| Australia | 31% |
| Malaysia | 22% |

SOURCE: IMF, WORLD BANK

# Supporting Question 1

FEATURED SOURCE Source A: An article describing the founding and power of chaebol, "Money, Power, Family: Inside South Korea's Chaebol," *The New York Times*, Carlos Tejada, February 17, 2017 (excerpt).

https://www.nytimes.com/2017/02/17/business/south-korea-chaebol-samsung.html

## What are chaebol?

The word [chaebol] comes from the combination of the characters for "rich" and "clan." It applies to large groups of interconnected companies that are usually dominated by a wealthy family. South Korea has several, but the best known outside the country are Hyundai, LG and Samsung. Others include Hanjin, Kumho, Lotte and SK Group.

Chaebol are generally conglomerates of affiliated companies. LG, for example, makes smartphones, televisions, electronic components, chemicals and fertilizer.

# Supporting Question 1

FEATURED SOURCE Source B: Bar graph showing the significant economic presence of chaebol in the South Korean economy, using data from the Korea Fair Trade Commission, excerpted from Kim Jaewon, "South Korea's Moon Vows to Rev Up Jobs and Rein in 'Chaebol,'" *Nikkei Asian Review*, May 18, 2017

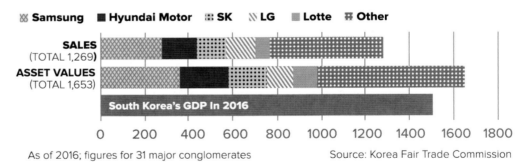

Chaebol's Huge Presence In South Korean Economy
(IN TRILLIONS OF WON)

Samsung  Hyundai Motor  SK  LG  Lotte  Other

SALES (TOTAL 1,269)
ASSET VALUES (TOTAL 1,653)
South Korea's GDP In 2016

0   200   400   600   800   1000   1200   1400   1600   1800

As of 2016; figures for 31 major conglomerates     Source: Korea Fair Trade Commission

## Supporting Question 2

**FEATURED SOURCE** Source A: Video about the numerous, diverse products Samsung produces, "How Samsung Dominates South Korea's Economy," 2017.

http://money.cnn.com/2017/02/17/technology/samsung-south-korea-daily-life/index.html

## Supporting Question 2

**FEATURED SOURCE** Source B: Rachel Premack, timeline detailing the development of Chaebols and the South Korean economy, "South Korea's Conglomerates," *Sage Business Researcher*, August 21, 2017.

http://businessresearcher.sagepub.com/sbr-1863-103804-2830718/20170821/south-koreas-conglomerates

| | |
|---|---|
| **1910–1987** | **From colonialism to development.** |
| 1910 | Neighboring Japan annexes the Korean Peninsula. |
| 1945 | Japan surrenders in World War II and its colonial rule in Korea ends. The Soviet Union and United States split the country in two, with the Soviet Union dominating the northern half and the United States the southern. They determine that the two Koreas should be reunited after four years and enjoy independent rule. |
| 1950–1953 | The Korean War begins when the North invades the South, then concludes in a stalemate, with no peace treaty signed. The estimates of total casualties, including military and civilians, range from 1.2 million to 5 million. South Korean President Syngman Rhee rules autocratically for the rest of the 1950s as the economy struggles. In the North, Communist strongman Kim Il-sung creates a Stalinist state. |
| 1963 | After seizing power in a military coup two years earlier, Park Chung-hee is elected president. During his 18-year rule, South Korea's economy is revolutionized at a deep cost to human rights. |
| 1972 | Under Park Chung-hee's direction, a young company, POSCO, opens its first modern steel plant. Skepticism abounds that South Korea should develop domestic heavy industries. POSCO is now the fifth-largest steel producer in the world. |
| 1981 | South Korea receives its last significant aid package from Japan, just under $800 million in 2010 U.S. dollars. Six years later, it begins granting development assistance to others. |
| 1987 | Ending decades of military dictatorships and crushed democracy movements, a democratic government is established in South Korea. The constitution, still in force today, provides for a free press, direct election of presidents and, among other rights, habeas corpus. |
| **1997–PRESENT** | **Crises and corruption charges amid global dominance.** |
| 1997 | South Korea is among the hardest hit by the Asian financial crisis. Its national debt-to-GDP ratio nearly doubles, its currency tumbles in value and its stock markets experience record drops. |

CONTINUED ON PAGE 160

| | |
|---|---|
| **1998** | Some chaebols and several affiliated firms go under as a result of the financial crisis. Daewoo, once a major force in buses, cars, shipbuilding, electronics and hotels, declares bankruptcy and splits into three smaller firms. Samsung Motors sells 80 percent of its stock to French automaker Renault. |
| **1999–2000** | Gross domestic product grows by 11.3 percent in 1999 and another 8.9 percent in 2000, marking a return to a flourishing economy. |
| **2010** | South Korea joins the Organization for Economic Co-operation and Development's Development Assistance Committee, a consortium of the world's biggest aid donors. South Korea is the first country to go from being a recipient of committee aid to a donating member. |
| **2012** | South Korea becomes the first newly industrialized country to join the "20–50 club" – countries with a population of more than 50 million that have a per capita income of more than $20,000. The other six are the United States, Germany, France, the United Kingdom, Italy and Japan. |
| **2016** | Approval ratings for President Park Geun-hye, who is Park Chung-hee's daughter, fall to 4 percent in late November. Details concerning allegations of influence peddling involving Park and confidante Choi Soon-sil emerge, prompting hundreds of thousands of Koreans to turn out for weekly protests demanding the imprisonment of Park, Choi and several chaebol leaders. |
| **2017** | Lee Jae-yong, the de facto head of Samsung Group and third-wealthiest person in Korea, is arrested in February. Samsung allegedly paid $36 million in bribes in 2015 to fraudulent charities operated by Choi. Park is arrested a month later. Moon Jae-in is elected president in May, the first liberal to win a presidential election in South Korea since 2002. |

## Supporting Question 2

**FEATURED SOURCE**  Source C: Staff writers, "The Death of Daewoo," detailing the failure of one chaebol, *The Economist*, August 19, 1999 (excerpt).

http://www.economist.com/node/233562

Daewoo's financial trouble came to a head only last month, but its failure was a long time coming. Last year, when the economic crisis forced most of the chaebol to cut back, Daewoo brazenly added 14 new firms to its existing 275 subsidiaries—and this in a year where the group lost a combined 550 billion won ($458m) on sales of 62 trillion won ($51 billion). At the end of 1997, South Korea's four biggest chaebol averaged debt of nearly five times their equity.

## Supporting Question 2

**FEATURED SOURCE**  Source D: Kim Jaewon, "South Korea's Moon Vows to Rev Up Jobs and Rein in 'Chaebol,'" detailing how the current South Korean President may want to limit the power of chaebol, *Nikkei Asian Review*, May 18, 2017 (excerpt).

https://asia.nikkei.com/magazine/20170518/On-the-Cover/South-Korea-s-Moon-vows-to-rev-up-jobs-and-rein-in-chaebol?page=2

He [Moon] singled out the four biggest conglomerates—Samsung, Hyundai Motor, SK and LG—as needing to be reined in, noting they account for about half of all assets held by the country's top 30 conglomerates.

Moon said the Lee family that owns Samsung, the country's largest conglomerate, has run the group like "an emperor," controlling all aspects of the business despite having only a limited stake, while taking no responsibility for its failures. He said the family's totalitarian style of leadership needs to make way for a democratic management run by professionals.

## Supporting Question 2

FEATURED SOURCE Source E: Sultan Sharrief, "The Legacy: A Documentary," Korean War Legacy Project; full-length, classroom-friendly, 40-minute documentary film.

https://koreanwarlegacy.org

USED WITH PERMISSION FROM THE KOREAN WAR LEGACY PROJECT

Minutes 23:05 to 25:55 of this documentary feature a description of the development of South Korea since the Korean War.

# Why Was the Korean War "Forgotten"?

Carly Muetterties and Kathy Swan

## WHY WAS THE KOREAN WAR "FORGOTTEN"?

| | |
|---|---|
| **C3 Framework Indicator** | **D2.His.5.9-12**. Analyze how historical contexts shaped and continued to shape people's perspectives. |
| **Staging the Compelling Question** | In October 1951, *US News & World Report* referred to the Korean War as the "Forgotten War." Using the image bank of Korean War monuments and the original article, discuss the factors that influence whether or not a historical event is considered memorable. |

| SUPPORTING QUESTION 1 | SUPPORTING QUESTION 2 | SUPPORTING QUESTION 3 | SUPPORTING QUESTION 4 |
|---|---|---|---|
| How did the Korean conflict become a "war"? | What domestic concerns distracted Americans from the war? | Did the soldiers forget? | How has U.S. history forgotten the Korean War? |
| **FORMATIVE PERFORMANCE TASK** | **FORMATIVE PERFORMANCE TASK** | **FORMATIVE PERFORMANCE TASK** | **FORMATIVE PERFORMANCE TASK** |
| Create an annotated timeline of the major events that led to the Korean War. | Write a paragraph that describes the domestic concerns that distracted Americans from the Korean conflict. | Write a claim supported by evidence about why soldiers believe the war was "forgotten." | Write an evidence-based claim or series of claims about how the Korean War has or has not been forgotten in U.S. history. |
| **FEATURED SOURCES** | **FEATURED SOURCES** | **FEATURED SOURCES** | **FEATURED SOURCES** |
| **Source A:** Korean War Legacy Project's Memory Bank timeline materials<br>**Source B:** Excerpt from Truman's radio speech supporting UN action in Korea, September 1, 1950<br>**Source C:** Excerpts from *Selling the Korean War*, Steven Casey<br>**Source D:** "Milestones Along the Road to Mobilization," *Pathfinder News Magazine*, January 10, 1951<br>**Source E:** Excerpt from Truman's presidential news conference about Korea, July 13, 1950 | Sources from Supporting Question 1, as well as:<br>**Source A:** Excerpts from *In the Shadow of the Greatest Generation*, Melinda L. Pash<br>**Source B:** Excerpts from "Truman's Other War," Paul G. Pierpaoli, Jr. | Sources from Supporting Questions 1 and 2, as well as:<br>**Source A:** Transcript of oral history interview, John Singhose<br>**Source B:** Transcript of oral history interview, James Warren<br>**Source C:** Transcript of oral history interview, Everett Kelley | Students' U.S. History textbooks |

| | |
|---|---|
| **Summative Performance Task** | **ARGUMENT** Construct an argument (e.g., detailed outline, poster, or essay) that discusses the compelling question using specific claims and relevant evidence from historical sources while acknowledging competing views.<br>**EXTENSION** Using claims from Supporting Question 4, propose a textbook revision reflecting research conducted in this inquiry and soldiers' perceptions of the war. |
| **Taking Informed Action** | **UNDERSTAND** Explore the Korean War Veterans' Digital Memorial (KWVDM) Interview Initiative and identify local veteran groups or other community members who are Korean War veterans.<br>**ASSESS** Determine the ways in which students can contribute to KWVDM's initiative.<br>**ACT** Create an oral history project to contribute to the KWVDM archives. |

# Overview
## Inquiry Description

This inquiry leads students through an investigation of how the Korean War came to be known as the "forgotten war." By investigating the compelling question "Why was the Korean War 'forgotten'?" students investigate how a major global event could seem to have been forgotten by the American public and, subsequently, in history. The inquiry has students consider the progression of the "conflict" to a "war," actions of those in power during Harry S. Truman's U.S. presidency, the views of veterans and those on the home front, and the portrayal of Korea in U.S. history textbooks. This leads students to questions about how the Korean War differed from previous and subsequent military engagements in terms of the remote threat it posed to the American people and an underlying Cold War sentiment that evolved from anti-communism to containment. Teachers should also help students understand how the process of "forgetting" the Korean War reflects geopolitical events as well as domestic concerns.

The formative performance tasks build on knowledge and skills through the course of the inquiry and help students recognize different perspectives in order to better understand the impacts of the Korean War on the home front. Students create an evidence-based argument about how the war was "forgotten," considering the ways in which daily life was affected, the concerns of the U.S. population at the time, and returning veterans' experiences.

This inquiry highlights the following C3 Dimension 2 Indicator:

> **D2.His.5.9-12**. Analyze how historical contexts shaped and continue to shape people's perspectives.

Some prerequisite knowledge of historical events and ideas is necessary for this inquiry. Thus, teachers will want to ensure their students are aware of the total war mobilization that occurred during World War II, the ways in which World War II mobilized the public by conceptualizing it as a war of fascism versus freedom, and the Cold War tensions that emerged in the post-war period.

This inquiry is expected to take four to seven 50-minute class periods. The inquiry time frame could expand if teachers think their students need additional instructional experiences (i.e., supporting questions, formative performance tasks, and featured sources). Inquiries are not scripts, so teachers are encouraged to modify and adapt them in order to meet the needs and interests of their particular students. Resources can also be modified as necessary to meet individualized education programs (IEPs) or Section 504 plans for students with disabilities.

## Structure of the Inquiry

In addressing the compelling question "Why was the Korean War 'forgotten'?" students work through a series of supporting questions, formative performance tasks, and featured sources in order to construct an argument supported by evidence while acknowledging competing perspectives.

## STAGING THE COMPELLING QUESTION

The compelling question could be staged by introducing students to the description of the Korean War as a "forgotten war" by *US News & World Report* in October 1951, as well as by guided viewing of the image bank of Korean War monuments that use the word "forgotten." Students can discuss the political, social, and/or cultural factors that influence the extent to which a historical event becomes more or less memorable, and also consider the populations most likely to remember it. The discussion should include a consideration of historical events that have occurred in the students' lives that are memorable to them and the factors that have caused them to be so. Additionally, students can discuss current events and the extent to which they believe these events will or will not be memorable. This staging could lead into a discussion of students' current knowledge of the Korean War.

## SUPPORTING QUESTION 1

The first supporting question is: "How did the Korean conflict become a 'war'?" It asks students to consider the progression of the Korean conflict to a war, and how this compared to mobilization during World War II. This formative performance task asks students to create an annotated timeline of the major events that led to the Korean War. Teachers should consider how mobilization affects public perception, including how it may foster public support for the war effort. Featured Source A is a set of timeline materials from the Korean War Legacy's Memory Bank on U.S. involvement in Korea. Featured Source B is a radio address by U.S. President Harry S. Truman calling on the American people to support a resolution by the United Nations to retaliate against the North Korean forces in order to remove them from Seoul; this source provides students with information on how the United States worked with supranational forces to mobilize for war. In Featured Source C, *Selling the Korean War*, author Steven Casey describes the actions of the Truman administration to minimize public fears to prevent the all-out war culture that existed in World War II. Featured Source D is a newspaper article from the period, which presents milestone events in the mobilization of the home front for the Korean War as well as changes to domestic life. Featured Source E is a transcript of President Truman's press conference of July 13, 1950 on the Korean "emergency."

## SUPPORTING QUESTION 2

The second supporting question is "What domestic concerns distracted Americans from the war?" To answer this question, students consider the most important domestic American issues during the Korean War era. The formative performance task has students write a summary that describes domestic concerns that distracted Americans from the war. Building on Supporting Question 1, students should consider the extent to which mobilization for the war did or did not make Korea a societal focus in light of these distractions. In the case of the Korean War, there was a lack of a clear concept of what threat a civil war in Korea posed to the United States. This contrasted sharply with World War II, which had a more clearly defined enemy (i.e., fascism and militarism). In addition to the resources from the previous supporting question, the two featured sources here provide students with additional materials that allow them to consider why the Korean War was just another news story, rather than the most pressing national concern. Featured Source A is an excerpt from Melinda Pash's *In the Shadow of the Greatest Generation*. Pash describes the very different home front mentalities during World War II and the Korean War, including the impact of the 1950s consumer culture. Featured Source B consists of excerpts from *Truman's Other War: The Battle for the American Homefront, 1950-1953*, by Paul G. Pierpaoli.

Pierpaoli presents the United States as being in a new "Cold War climate" in which the Korean War played a part, but was not the centerpiece; he also argues that the Korean War became a part of the larger, permanent mobilization of the Cold War, thereby lessening its individual significance to many Americans. Additionally, teachers may supplement this question with sources related to other domestic issues (e.g., McCarthyism and consumer culture).

## SUPPORTING QUESTION 3

The third supporting question—"Did the soldiers forget? —asks students to consider the ways soldiers reflect on their wartime experiences. Students will write a claim supported by evidence about why soldiers believe the war was "forgotten." In addition to the previous featured sources, the sources for this task will show the perspectives of three soldiers who served in Korea in interview transcripts from the Korean War Veterans Digital Memorial (KWVDM). Though three interview transcripts are included here, teachers are encouraged to have students explore other interviews to add to this supporting question.

## SUPPORTING QUESTION 4

In the fourth supporting question—"How has U.S. history forgotten the Korean War?"— students will evaluate their U.S. History textbooks to consider the extent to which they discuss Korea or whether the Korean War is eclipsed by coverage of other topics (e.g., World War II, the larger Cold War, the Vietnam War, and/or other topics from Supporting Question 2). The formative performance task asks students to write an evidence-based claim or series of claims about how the Korean War has or has not been forgotten in U.S. history. For this task, students should use their own textbooks, but teachers may wish to supplement these with other available texts to provide a more inclusive assessment.

## SUMMATIVE PERFORMANCE TASK

At this point in the inquiry, students have examined the ways in which the United States mobilized for the Korean War, the extent to which this had an impact on the home front, how veterans view the war, and U.S. History textbook depictions. Students should be expected to demonstrate the breadth of their understanding and their ability to use evidence from multiple sources to support their claims. In this task, students construct an evidence-based argument using multiple sources to answer the compelling question "Why was the Korean War 'forgotten'?" It is important to note that students' arguments could take a variety of forms, including a detailed outline, poster, or essay.

Students' arguments will vary, but could include any of the following:

- The Korean War was "forgotten" because it started as a police action and slowly progressed to a conflict.

- The Korean War was "forgotten" because Americans were focused on other domestic issues facing the country (e.g., consumerism and the economy).

- The Korean War was "forgotten" because veterans came home to a different social climate than soldiers returning from World War II, leaving many to remain relatively silent about their wartime experiences.

- The Korean War was "forgotten" because it is often eclipsed in textbooks by World War II, the Vietnam War, the larger Cold War, and other domestic concerns.

Students could extend these arguments by using their claims from Supporting Question 4 to propose a textbook revision. This should reflect the research they conducted in this inquiry and soldiers' perceptions of the war.

Students have the opportunity to take informed action by drawing on their understandings of the value of preserving historical events in different mediums, particularly oral histories. To *understand*, students can explore the Korean War Veterans Digital Memorial Interview Initiative and identify local veteran groups or other community members that are Korean War veterans. To *assess* the issue, students determine the ways in which they can contribute to the initiative. To *act*, students contribute to the oral history project for the KWVDM archives.

## Staging the Compelling Question

**FEATURED SOURCE**    Unknown author, newspaper article, "Korea: The 'Forgotten' War," *US News & World Report*, October 5, 1951, p. 21 (excerpt).

Far off in Korea, 2,200 American men were killed or badly shot up last week in a war that seemed all but forgotten at home. War that was supposed to end in a deal with Communists instead is growing in intensity.

Ground battles, for the area involved, are as intense as those of any war. Air battles, against fliers of unknown nationality, are approaching in size some of those of World War II. Casualties have increased from an annual rate of 50,000 to more than 100,000. That's the equivalent of 1 boy in every 10 coming of military age now.

At home, meanwhile, the big headlines concern a growing shortage of beef, graft scandals in the government, strikes as usual, prospects of a new-car scarcity.

Korea, half forgotten, is receding in the minds of many to the status of an experimental war, one being fought back and forth for the purpose of testing men, weapons, materials and methods, on a continuing basis.

# Staging the Compelling Question

FEATURED SOURCE Image bank: Korean War memorials.

https://cdn.lib.unc.edu/commemorative-landscapes/media/monument/475_full.jpg

### Fayetteville, North Carolina
CUMBERLAND COUNTY KOREAN WAR MEMORIAL, FAYETTEVILLE, NC, COURTESY OF DANIEL N. JOURDAN

https://commons.wikimedia.org/wiki/File:Korean_War_memorial_Auburn.jpg

### Auburn, New York
WIKIMEDIA COMMONS, BEYOND MY KEN

Greenville, South Carolina
KOREAN WAR VETERANS ASSOCIATION INC., FOOTHILLS CHAPTER OF SC #301

Olympia, Washington
WASHINGTON STATE DEPARTMENT ENTERPRISE SERVICES

# Supporting Question 1

Source A: Korean War Legacy, "Memory Bank," timeline.

CHAPTERS

Changing the Game at Incheon

Holding the Pusan Perimeter

Postwar Perceptions

Korea: Forgetting and Remembering

Multiple Perspectives on the Korean War

North Koreans Stream Toward Pusan

Recapturing Seoul

Prewar Context: Western

Significance of the May 1948 Election

The Human Experience

African-Americans in the Korean War

North Toward the Yalu River

POW Experience

The Psychological Impact of Combat

What To Do About Prisoners of War

USED WITH PERMISSION FROM THE KOREAN WAR LEGACY PROJECT

# Supporting Question 1

FEATURED SOURCE Source B: Harry S. Truman, transcript from radio speech about the support for UN action in Korea, September 1, 1950.

https://www.trumanlibrary.org

First: We believe in the United Nations. When we ratified its Charter, we pledged ourselves to seek peace and security through this world organization. We kept our word when we went to the support of the United Nations in Korea two months ago. We shall never go back on that pledge.

Second: We believe the Koreans have a right to be free, independent, and united—as they want to be. Under the direction and guidance of the United Nations, we, with others, will do our part to help them enjoy that right. The United States has no other aim in Korea.

Third: We do not want the fighting in Korea to expand into a general war. It will not spread unless communist imperialism draws other armies and governments into the fight of the aggressors against the United Nations.

USED WITH PERMISSION FROM THE TRUMAN LIBRARY

# Supporting Question 1

FEATURED SOURCE Source C: Excerpts from a book published in 2008 by Steven Casey, *Selling the Korean War: Propaganda, Politics, and Public Opinion in the United States, 1950-1953* (New York: Oxford University Press, 2008).

Fearful that this new Cold War crisis might escalate into a far bigger conflict with the Soviet Union, the president and his senior advisers sought to keep the home front cool. They made few public statements. And what they did say was carefully restrained. (p. 19)

"Don't make it alarmist" became something of a motif for [President Truman's] early information campaign. As one shrewd observer [*US News & World Report*] noted at the time, "the real idea was to fix in the public eye a picture of the government in a calm mood... to keep Korea in its place: a pint-sized incident, not a full-scale war. [...] Official Washington was doing everything it could to keep a firm line against the communists, and keep the home front cool at the same time." (p. 20)

But all of a sudden, one question [at a press conference, June 29, 1950] brought a typically quick-fire response. "Mr. President, everybody is asking in this country, "Are we, or are we not, at war?" "We are not at war," Truman emphatically declared, a statement he allowed reporters to quote directly. Anxious to get something more substantial, another journalist then prompted Truman with a trick that periodically worked at his press conferences: he put words into the president's mouth. Would it be correct "to call this a police action under the UN?," he inquired. "Yes," Truman replied, "that is exactly what it amounts to." (p. 28)

As news of battlefield defeats hit home, the administration tried to channel the public debate on how America ought to mobilize in this new, more dangerous phase of the Cold War. The instinct of Truman and his senior advisers was to remain cautious: they were still keen to stop the domestic mood from overheating, lest this result in overpowering demands to escalate the Cold War, perhaps even by launching a preventive strike against the Soviet Union. (p. 67)

Until now, domestic pressures had also seemed to stand in the way of a large defense buildup. Before Korea, Congress had clearly been in a stingy mood, and it had escaped no one's notice back in January when Truman's State of the Union address had been noisily interrupted from both sides of the aisle as soon as he proposed that "federal expenditures be held to the lowest levels." Nor, more generally, did the mass of Americans seem willing to embrace the sacrifices necessary for a sustained mobilization. During the spring, even champions of NSC-68 [a critical, top-secret memorandum about national security, written by the U.S. government in 1950] had been pessimistic about the prospect of persuading a majority of the public to support their rearmament ideas, convinced that the popular mood was basically volatile, with many Americans all too willing to lapse periodically into a state of apathy and complacency. "I fear that the U.S. public would rapidly tire of such an effort," Edward Barrett [Assistant Secretary of State for Public Affairs] had gloomily noted in April. (p. 68)

The president's call [Fireside Chat, July 19, 1950] for limited economic controls was also far less radical than some officials seemed to want. (p. 70)

[Truman] doubtless recalled the deep hostility toward wage and price regulation during World War II, when the Office of Price Administration had become "a target for all the frustrations and disappointments of people unaccustomed to regimentation and control," not to mention the 1946 midterm elections, when Republicans had successfully campaigned on a platform to swiftly terminate wartime controls. Unwilling to return to such an unpopular path in the current limited emergency, Truman concurred with his political and economic advisers, like Averell Harriman and Leon Keyserling, who "were profoundly convinced that the country and Congress were not yet ready for an all-out mobilization bill." Consequently, all that appeared in the administration's defense production measure were powers to allow the president to allocate resources and facilities for the buildup, to control consumer credit and commodity speculation, and to provide loans to small businesses to help them participate in the production of military hardware. That the administration's mobilization plan was distinctly limited would naturally become a focal point for all the public explanations during the coming weeks. The president would not ask for sweeping powers "until he thinks they are essential and that Congress would grant them," Dr. John Steelman, assistant to the president, told one *Time* reporter in a background briefing. "That wouldn't be until we are in a real emergency and I wouldn't say that we are in such an emergency now." "We are not, at this time, calling for an all-out mobilization," Symington explained. (p. 70)

Inside the White House, meanwhile, Truman remained anxious to avoid any action that might engender or exacerbate a "war psychosis" among the American public. (p. 72)

[Assistant Secretary of State for Public Affairs] Barrett stressed that: "the mobilization for which he [the president] is asking is for the purpose of replacing the wastage in Korea and generally improving the defense of the United States. It does not constitute full war mobilization. He therefore feels that in the passage cited it would be desirable not to relate the measures now being taken to the expectation of general war." (p. 72)

# Supporting Question 1

**FEATURED SOURCE**   Source D: "Milestones Along the Road to Mobilization," *Pathfinder News Magazine*, January 10, 1951.

http://www.oldmagazinearticles.com/article-summary/korean-war-mobilization#.WC9NQuErl1g

## Milestones along the road to mobilization

Six months after Korea had jerked the U.S. onto the road toward mobilization, the nation could count these accomplishments:

**Manpower**. The Army's 10 pre-Korea divisions, none at full strength, brought to 11, plus 4 National Guard Divisions and 2 Guard regimental combat teams called into Federal service. Monthly draft for January, February and March set at 80,000, bringing the total since K-day to 450,000. Faster induction stymied by shortages of training cadres [and] some equipment. Doctors, dentists and veterinarians under 50 were told to register Jan. 15. Some 210,000 face possible military service.

**Resources**. Cobalt, vital in steel making and electronics, put under complete Government allocations [on] Dec. 29—first strategic material so controlled. By March television and radio sets will be using cobalt substitutes in speakers; finishes on refrigerators and other civilian products will be affected by diversion of cobalt from paint making to defense.

There'll be fewer pots and pans; more glass containers on grocery shelves—allotments of aluminum, tin, zinc, copper, and other materials for civilian use were cut back 20% to 50%. Natural rubber for tires and other products [was] curbed. Government on Dec. 28 became rubber's sole importer and distributor; it already owns most of the synthetic rubber production facilities. Ban on hoarding—by civilians as well as industry—declared for 55 scarce metals: Inventory controls and basic rules for priorities system set up.

**Price control**. Automobile prices rolled back to Dec. 1 levels; 250 other manufacturers asked to give Government seven days' notice of intended price increases. Voluntary co-operation of all businesses asked in holding down prices. Economic Stabilization Agency, which handles wage and price control, announced it would set up regional offices by March, expects by then to have "500 or 600 employees." (OPA in World War II had 250,000, all but 64,000 of whom were volunteers.)

**Wage control**. Wages for automobile workers frozen until Mar. 1 (under auto industry's labor contract, tied to cost-of-living index, no wage increase would have been scheduled until that date anyway). Five labor and four business leaders meet Jan. 10 with ESA officials to discuss a nation-wide wage formula.

**Construction**. New theaters, amusement places and other "nonessential or recreational" construction barred. Home buying regulations toughened. Rent control extended to Mar. 31.

**Credit**. Down payments increased, time in which to pay shortened for installment buying of autos, furniture, household appliances and other products. The Federal Reserve System announced an increase in reserve requirements for member banks. (They do 85% of the nation's lending business.) This would cut about $12 billion in lending power, make it harder for business and individuals to get loans.

**Civil Defense**. All states and major metropolitan areas have appointed civil defense directors. A dozen cities have held, or will hold, attack-rehearsal programs. New York is recruiting 500,000 civil defense volunteers and may turn subways into bomb shelters. Nation-wide air raid warning signals were established. Manuals on atomic attack and bacteriological and chemical warfare [were] distributed. Last week Congress approved a civil defense bill setting up [an] independent agency whose director, on Presidential declaration of an emergency, would have almost unlimited power to seize equipment and facilities and mobilize the entire Federal Government to aid stricken areas.

**Administration**. Newly set-up war agencies start building staffs. Civil Defense last week had 99 employees, plans ultimately to have 5,000. National Production Authority sees tenfold increase from present 1,000 by September. Altogether Federal employment since K-day has increased 200,000; within six months 300,000 more will be added to the public payroll. The number of public employees last October had reached 6.4 million—just under the World War II record level. They drew $1.5 billion a month in pay.

ARTICLE PROVIDED COURTESY OF OLDMAGAZINEARTICLES.COM

## Supporting Question 1

FEATURED SOURCE    Source E: Excerpt from Harry S. Truman's 231st Presidential News Conference, in which the president addressed a standing-room-only crowd to answer questions about the Korean "emergency," Indian Treaty Room (Room 474) in the Executive Office Building, Washington, DC, July 13, 1950.

https://www.trumanlibrary.org/publicpapers/index.php?pid=820&st=&st1

**THE PRESIDENT**. I have no particular announcements to make, but I will try to answer questions so far as I can.

**Q.** Mr. President, is there anything you could tell us about plans for any partial industrial mobilization—

**Voices**: Can't hear—can't hear.

**THE PRESIDENT**. He wanted to know if there were any plans about industrial mobilization. All the things that relate to the emergency are under consideration, and at the proper time the necessary steps will be taken if they are necessary. I want to say directly that they are under consideration.

**Q.** Well, specifically, Mr. President, Senator Thomas yesterday said that he expects that there will be a request for a billion additional [dollars] for military expenditures in a week or so—?

**THE PRESIDENT**. Since the figures have not been assembled and presented to the President of the United States, we can't give any definite figure.

**Q.** Mr. President, may I just give you one more [question]?

**THE PRESIDENT**. Sure, fire away.

**Q.** May we expect, though, that there will be a request for additional military expenditures in the next week or so?

**THE PRESIDENT**. It is under consideration.

**Q.** Mr. President, sir, do you still call this a "police action"?

**THE PRESIDENT.** Yes, it is still a police action.

**Q.** Mr. President, are we prepared to resist aggression everywhere in the world, as in Korea?

**THE PRESIDENT.** We will have to meet the situations as they develop. I can't answer that question.

[ ... ]

**THE PRESIDENT.** Did you have a question?

**Q.** Yes, sir, thank you. Can you say anything about mobilization plans, sir, not industrial/manpower?

**THE PRESIDENT.** All those things are under consideration, and I can't make any statements on them at the present time. You will be kept informed of all the procedures as they come about.

**Q.** Mr. President, are you planning any report to Congress, or to the people, on the Korean situation?

**THE PRESIDENT.** That is under consideration, too. No decision has been reached.

**Q.** Mr. President, would you give us an evaluation now of the fighting so far in Korea, from your point of view?

**THE PRESIDENT.** No. I am not in charge of the military in Korea, and the report is made every day by General MacArthur, and he is the one to evaluate the situation. I rely on his evaluation.

**Q.** Well, Mr. President, can you comment in general on the outlook in Korea? Last week you said you were hopeful—

**THE PRESIDENT.** I feel the same way. My position has not changed on that at all.

**Q.** Are you anything more than hopeful, sir? What I mean is—

**THE PRESIDENT.** What do you mean by that?

**Q.** It does require clarification. We all get queries from our home offices—

**THE PRESIDENT.** Sure.

**Q.** —on the communiqués. What reassurance can we give the American people that we are not getting the tar licked out of us?

**THE PRESIDENT.** We are going to—

**Q.** Can't hear, sir.

**THE PRESIDENT.** Let me tell you something—

**Q.** We can't hear.

**THE PRESIDENT.** He wanted to know what assurance we could give the American people that we aren't getting the tar licked out of us. It has never happened to us. It won't happen this time.

**Q.** In that connection, Mr. President, do you feel certain that we will be able to retain a foothold in Korea?

**THE PRESIDENT.** We will be able to retain a foothold in Korea as far north as the 38th parallel.

**Q.** Mr. President, does that mean that we don't intend to carry our police action north of the 38th parallel?

**THE PRESIDENT.** I will make that decision when it becomes necessary to do it.

**Q.** Thank you.

**Q.** Mr. President, any news on the Mexican loan?

**THE PRESIDENT.** No. There is one thing I would like very much to impress on you, if you will bear with me about a minute. There is no prospect of any food shortage in this country at any time. We have in prospect one of the largest corn crops we have ever had, and had a billion bushels carried over. We have a normal cotton crop in prospect, and there are 3 million bales in storage in the hands of the Commodity Credit Corporation. We expect as large a wheat crop as we had last year, and anticipate as large a one next year, and there are some 700 million bushels of wheat in the carryover. So there is nothing to worry about, so far as food and things of that sort are concerned. I wish you would make that perfectly plain to your subscribers.

**Q.** Mr. President, we talked to [Secretary of Agriculture Charles F.] Brannan this morning about that, and he said it would be a reasonable deduction that rising prices would be due to profiteering. Do you agree with that?

**THE PRESIDENT.** I do. The statement I just made you would show that that is true. I discussed the matter with Secretary Brannan this morning, too. [Laughter]

**Q.** He denied it.

**Q.** Would you like to comment on the hoarding, Mr. President?

**THE PRESIDENT.** I beg your pardon?

**Q.** There are reports of hoarding of food and various other commodities. Would you like to make a statement?

**THE PRESIDENT.** I think it is very foolish to start anything of that kind now. There is no necessity for it whatever, as I am trying to make perfectly plain to you.

**Q.** Mr. President, would your remarks apply also to consumer goods, like automobiles and other—

**THE PRESIDENT.** I can't comment on any of those things, because I am only talking of the things that I know definitely about.

**Q.** Mr. President, there is a report from Geneva from the International Red Cross, I think, that they have sent a man to North Korea to see that they recognize the rules of warfare—?

**THE PRESIDENT.** I haven't had any such report, but I am sure that General [George C.] Marshall [president of the American National Red Cross] will see that that is done.

**Q.** Thank you, sir.

**Q.** Mr. President, you were asked earlier about consideration of either going before the Congress or the people on the Korean situation. Did you mean that to say that you were considering both, or one or the other?

**THE PRESIDENT.** Yes, both.

**Q.** Thank you, sir.

**THE PRESIDENT.** I am considering everything in connection with this situation which I think will be helpful in keeping the American people and the Congress informed on what goes on.

**Q.** Mr. President, are we doing anything to urge the participation of ground troops of other nations in—

**THE PRESIDENT.** That question was answered by Secretary Acheson yesterday. If you will read his report at the press conference, you will get your answer.

**Q.** Mr. President, do you plan to ask for an increase in taxes?

**THE PRESIDENT.** I have no tax plans. The statement of the Secretary of Agriculture covered all that I can say about the matter at this time.

**Q.** Treasury, Mr. President.

**THE PRESIDENT.** I mean Secretary of the Treasury, yes. I was thinking about Brannan.

**Q.** Can you say anything about contingent reports that you might call up reserve officers and specialists, or mobilize the National Guard ?

**THE PRESIDENT.** All those things are under consideration. If it is necessary, announcements will be made in plenty of time so that you will all know about it.

**Q.** Mr. President, on the basis of what you said about food a minute ago, you mean that there is no contemplation of rationing being necessary in food?

**THE PRESIDENT.** Not at all.

**Q.** Mr. President, in view of the present situation, is there anything to speed up the machinery of the North Atlantic Pact being urged also on the other partners?

**THE PRESIDENT.** That is a matter on which I can't comment at this time.

PROVIDED COURTESY OF THE AMERICAN PRESIDENCY PROJECT. JOHN WOOLLEY AND GERHARD PETERS. UNIVERSITY OF CALIFORNIA, SANTA BARBARA. USED WITH PERMISSION FROM THE TRUMAN LIBRARY

## Supporting Question 2

**FEATURED SOURCE**   Source A: Excerpts from a book by Melinda L. Pash, *In the Shadow of the Greatest Generation: The Americans Who Fought the Korean War,* 2012 (New York: NYU Press, 2012).

Unlike their older brothers and cousins who served in World War II and returned to ticker-tape parades and welcoming bands, Korean War veterans returned quickly to a country that in their absence scarcely missed them. Though Americans initially rallied to the war drum when President Harry S. Truman called on the nation to defend South Korea from communist aggression, the lack of meaningful home-front participation in the form of rationing or other personal sacrifice soon made Korea only a minor distraction for the American public. As soldiers still green to battle clung to the Pusan Perimeter, as marines fought their way out of Chosin Reservoir with frozen feet and staggering casualties, and as GIs tried to hold the line in a bloody stalemate half a world away, Americans at home went on with their business as usual, concentrating on making the most of the prosperous post-World War II economy. Fearing wartime shortages, they snapped up furniture and televisions, refrigerators and cars. In Fords and Lincolns and Chevrolets, the war drove right out of the minds of many Americans and into the middle and back pages of newspapers. Returning veterans could only wonder at the world that seemingly had forgotten them, surprised that "there was no evidence that the civilian population of the USA even knew (or cared) that those of us getting off the ship had seen desperate combat" [quoting Robert Henderson, Korean War Veteran Survey, 9, Center for the Study of the Korean War, Graceland University, Independence, Missouri]. (p. 1)

Perhaps understandably, average Americans found themselves too busy to pay attention to the conflict raging thousands of miles away in Korea or to the soldiers trickling home, but movie makers, novelists, and even historians proved no better at acknowledging the sacrifices made by those American servicemen and women. Throughout the war and in the years following, Hollywood produced a number of war movies, but most of them looked back to the "good war," World War II, for inspiration. (p. 2)

Ten- and eleven-year-old kids when the Japanese bombed Pearl Harbor, [the Korean War generation] saw Americans join together to back the war effort, even if that meant making grave sacrifices. Sixteen million American men stepped into military uniforms ready to do their duty and lay down their lives in defense of the country and the values for which it stood. Those on the home front did their part, too. Whole towns turned out to say goodbye to their native sons being shipped off to war. Ordinary Americans, even young ones, grew Victory Gardens, saved scrap metal and paper, bought war stamps and war bonds, harvested milkweed pod for parachute making, and patriotically rallied behind their government. [...] When asked to conserve [for World War II], Americans accepted severe rationing of gasoline, meat, butter, sugar, and flour, and they continued to support the war. For hundreds of thousands of kids, the message must have been clear; in a time of war American citizens rally together, sharing the sacrifices and keeping the trust with those whom they called to serve. (p. 10)

As the [Korean] war dragged on, however, public interest and support waned. [...] The buying frenzy that had characterized 1950, when people still worried that war would directly affect their ability to purchase sugar, shortening, or televisions, had drawn to a close, leaving Americans free to concentrate on things other than the war effort. Headlines concerning strikes, domestic events, and even UFOs, rather than war news, monopolized the front pages of most newspapers. (p. 30)

Aside from a lack of political recognition, the troops in Korea had other reasons to feel like the home front had abandoned and forgotten them. Every day Americans laid down their lives in service to country on the Korean Peninsula, but back in the States people seemed completely disinterested in the war. Front-page headlines advertised "a growing shortage of beef, graft scandals in the Government, strikes as usual, [and] prospects of a new-car scarcity."

The war just did not seem all that newsworthy after the early months and especially once it stalemated. As editorial cartoonist Bill Mauldin noted of the Korean War infantryman, "He fights a battle in which his best friends get killed and if an account of the action gets printed at all in his home town paper, it appears on page 17 under a Lux ad." And, more than not paying attention to the war, people on the home front actually compromised the ability of men and women to carry out their duties in Korea—at least from the perspective of those in the war zone. Strikes and the attention paid them not only distracted Americans but deprived men in the field of the supplies they needed. Shortages at home meant the rationing of things like ammunition and equipment in the war zone. Of one strike a frustrated GI in theater wrote, "We felt it very definitely in the shortage of supplies and especially of equipment for several days. It woke me up to how closely connected all the fronts we battle on are. You begin to wonder if the old country realizes there's a war going on over here." Similarly, returning from Korea, another serviceman asserted, "Strikes at home make the GI feel … that people are so preoccupied with their own self-interests that they seem to have forgotten that we are fighting a war. The shortages due to the shipping strike in New York last autumn could be felt in Korea within two weeks." (pp. 125-126)

## Supporting Question 2

FEATURED SOURCE     Source B: Paul G. Pierpaoli, Jr., magazine article, "Truman's Other War: The Battle for the American Homefront, 1950-53," *OAH Magazine of History* 14(3), pp. 15-19, 2000 (excerpt).

Prior to 25 June 1950, President Harry S. Truman had no notion of fighting a major land war in Asia or, for that matter, engaging the nation in a vast and exorbitant Cold War rearmament program. In his January 1949 inaugural address, the president—always a rather staunch fiscal conservative—had promised to balance the budget, decrease the national debt, keep inflation at bay, and implement his Fair Deal program, an ambitious social welfare plan that sought to address an array of problems from public housing and health care to civil rights.

To accomplish this, Truman cast his lot with those who sought to keep national security and defense spending to a bare minimum. He also sought to provide America's allies with protection from the perceived Russian threat by using the strength of the U.S. economy as a bulwark against Communism. Thus, initiatives such as the Marshall Plan, the International Monetary Fund, and the General Agreement on Tariffs and Trade (GATT) would emphasize economic— rather than military—containment of the Soviet Union.

## Supporting Question 3

FEATURED SOURCE     Source A: John Singhose, transcript of an oral interview for the Korean War Veterans Digital History Project (excerpt).

**Interviewer**: When you left Korea, what did you think about the future of Korea? Did you have any idea how Korea would develop? Did you have any thought about it?

**John Singhose**: No, I had no idea what it was going to be like. It's unbelievable really. I've seen a lot of pictures, I've talked to a lot of these folks that have been over there and visited, but I know one thing, that the Korean people were very industrious, good, honest, hard workers.

**Interviewer**: How did you know?

**JS**: They worked with us. We had workers with us, too.

**Interviewer**: What were you thinking about you being there? I mean, you didn't know where Korea was—not much, right?

**JS**: No.

**Interviewer**: And, when you left Korea, you didn't think about the future of Korea? You didn't have any idea? Now, you're back in your home and looking at all of those things happening in Korea, what do you think about the whole thing?

**JS**: I think it's a great thing they've done. They're a great industrial power, and I've talked with a lot of folks from Korea since then, and I'm really impressed with them. I'm impressed with the country. I'm impressed with the people.

**Interviewer**: Why do you think we were able to pull this off?

**JS**: Well, I know they had help from the United States and Great Britain, and other countries there. We had people from Turkey there, Ethiopia, Canada. The Canadians were very helpful, also, working with the Koreans.

**Interviewer**: But despite such a clearly successful outcome out of the Korean War, why do you think the Korean War has been regarded as forgotten?

**JS**: Well, a lot of people seem to have forgotten it, but a lot of us haven't forgotten it.

**Interviewer**: Why [not]?

**JS**: Well, when I'm visiting with Ray, a lot of times we would discuss what we did over there.

**Interviewer**: What did you do there?

**JS**: I was a construction foreman, but I ran a bulldozer for a good part of the time. I did demolition work, too.

**Interviewer**: Now looking back all those years, what do you think you did for Korea?

**JS**: We trained a lot of their people, for one thing. I had always hoped to make contact with this Kim J. Ku and I had his address there [in Korea] and one of the fellows from the Korean Embassy was going to see if he could look him up, but I never heard anything back.

**Interviewer**: What was the most difficult thing? Was there something you really hated while you were in Korea?

**JS**: The extreme weather, probably, but we had clothing and whatever. We were good. The weather was probably the worst, but we worked with other units, the Marine Corps and the Turkish people. I didn't work with the Ethiopians, but Ray did. I thought it was kind of good. I worked with Canadians, too. It was good to work with those other people—a good learning experience.

**Interviewer**: What do you want to say to the Korean people now? Is there any message that you want to convey?

**JS**: I would like to congratulate them on the great job they did rebuilding the country, [and] the road networks they put in. The roads we put in were more or less just trails. But I think they have done a great job there. I would be the first to tell them that. I told a lot of the folks from the Korean Embassy that we met with from time to time.

**Interviewer**: So you don't regret your service there?

**JS**: Oh no, not at all. I learned a lot.

## Supporting Question 3

FEATURED SOURCE    Source B: James Warren, transcript of an oral interview for the Korean War Digital History Project (excerpt).

**Interviewer**: What were some of the most difficult, dangerous, rewarding, and happiest memories that you recall from your stay?

**James Warren**: Meeting my wife was probably the best—you know, meeting a lot of good people, meeting my best friend. Being able to experience [Korea]. I had been to Japan with the military and I was in Korea, and I found Korea to be better than Japan in the people sense.... The Korean people seemed to be more friendly than the Japanese people. It was easy to talk to them, [they were] easy to get along with and always helpful and friendly, and I enjoyed that. One of the things I did as a photographer [happened when] we had a Change of Command ceremony, the commander of the Second Infantry Division at the time was General Jeffrey Smith, and he was getting ready to be reassigned back to the States. They had assigned a new general coming from the States to take over the Second Infantry Division, so what they wanted me to do as a photographer was to go to every camp in the Second Infantry Division and photograph something significant to that camp. For example, if I went to this camp over here and it was primarily composed of infantry people, then I would take some [pictures of] things that would symbolize infantry. If I went to another camp filled with artillery soldiers, then I would take pictures that pertained to field artillery. And I did that for all the Second Infantry Divisions and [by] going up to the DMV and photographing things. The purpose of that was to brief the new general once he arrived in Korea by debriefing—showing him different places that were going to be under his command.

**Interviewer**: What was the impact of you being stationed in Korea, and did it impact your life at all after you returned home—besides the fact that you met your wife?

**JW**: That was probably the biggest impact of all.

**Interviewer**: Is there anything that you learned or that you took with you from Korea, or from [the experience of] being surrounded by the Korean people?

**JW**: I'm sure I probably was impacted in more ways than I could think of at the time, but what I really appreciate about the Korean people even today is their closeness and their values—like, all Koreans are friends to each other, that I have experienced, and we need to have more of that in all people. Especially in my race of people, we need to have more of that family [or] friend feel, like in relationships. So I learned that from meeting people and working with Korean people while I was stationed in Korea.

**Interviewer**: Have you been back to Korea?

**JW**: I was stationed there twice, and have not been back. My wife went back many times, but I did not go with her or anything like that and she communicated with family by telephone. I met some of the family while I was stationed there, but I haven't been back. That was probably one of the things that we were going to look at doing if [my wife] got better, health-wise.

**Interviewer**: In 2013 we witnessed the sixtieth anniversary of the armistice, which was signed by China, North Korea, and the UN on July 27, 1953. There is no war in modern history that has lasted sixty years after an official cease fire. What do you think we have to do to put a closure on it?

**JW**: You know, I don't know. To close it you have to put the country back together and not have a North and South—just [a unified] Korea. I don't know how you could achieve that. North Korea is not going to say, "Here you go!," and they are not going to negotiate, so I don't know. I don't know what you could do. I wish I could answer that question.

**Interviewer**: Would you support some kind of movement to petition for the end of war officially? Or maybe replace the armistice with a peace treaty?

**JW**: That is a hard one. Because, if you have North and South agreeing to things— "you do your thing, and I'll do my thing"—that probably would work out, but you cannot trust North Korea. My understanding is the North wants to be unified so if South Korea was satisfied and said, "Just give me a peace treaty; we will let them [in North Korea] live their life and we [in South Korea] will live our life," the North would not go forward with that. They would all be instigating doing things. So I would say, "So, let the armistice continue until such time as the country can be unified," and in the end you will have peace.

**Interviewer**: Do you think it is important for younger generations to understand what the Korean War was, and that it is still going on today, unofficially?

**JW**: Yes. This is my understanding of the Korean War Veterans Association's mission. The Korean War is called the "Forgotten War." It is the mission of the Korean War Veterans Association to not let the people forget that. Many people died and sacrificed, so you just can't forget that. The Korean [War] soldiers are dying out now, so when they're gone, the memory of what they did will be gone. So what they [at the KWVA] have done is incorporate people like me who served in Korea but who didn't serve in the Korean War so we can keep their story alive, so that it won't be forgotten. They do things to try to keep in the public eye so that it is not a forgotten war, and should never be a forgotten war. They do things like a program called Tell America, where they go into schools and they tell [students] about the Korean War and the things they did in the Korean War. They have received a lot of great response from that. So they must, it's historical and all history must be repeated, so people won't forget it and repeat it.

**Interviewer**: Why do you think the Korean War is known as the Forgotten War?

**JW**: I really don't know. First of all, we came out of World War II and people were tired and war weary, and not too long after that we entered the Korean War, and because it wasn't so much a "win" situation but [instead a division of the country into] North and South, it's easy to be placed under World War I and World War II. The main reason it's forgotten is that they never really called it a war. It was kind of like a police action. We use "police action" and stuff, and if you view the phrase over time and say it's a police action and it's actually not a war, well, people are going to remember a war but not a police action. And people forget that when they talk about war sometimes, so that's why I think it's forgotten. But by being in the association, I know those guys who were in the air doing things, on the ship doing things, and on the ground doing things, and I've heard their stories. I mean, it's a story worth retelling.

**Interviewer**: Earlier, you mentioned something about the legacy of Korean War veterans. What do you think that legacy is?

**JW**: That the people who fought and died, and the people who sacrificed, would not be forgotten. I think that's the legacy.

**Interviewer**: [Why] do you think the Korean War Veterans digital memorial that we are doing here, interviewing veterans, is important?

**JW**: It's very important because it serves to remind us of the war that we don't want to be forgotten. It is a tribute to those who made the ultimate sacrifice. And to those who fought and lived, it's a tribute to those who supported that. It is not always the guy on the ground or the guy flying in the air, it's all the support for the guys who are doing it. It is a tribute to all of those who had anything to do with the Korean War. Let me just say this about the [South] Korean people: they are truly thankful for what the Korean War veterans did to make their country a free country and the way it is. They express it all the time. They express it here in church, because they honor those veterans here every year. We have been to activities in Dallas [Texas] where they reiterated how much they appreciate what the Korean War veterans have done for their country, what it is today and stuff. When you hear those people say that, you know they are saying it from the heart.

**Interviewer**: Is there anything else that you would like to share, maybe memories or messages or something to do with your occupation that you would like to have preserved?

**JW**: The most important is when I re-enlisted in the military, I was a young man who had no idea what he wanted to do with himself. I was contemplating whether or not I should go to college, or should I just get myself a regular job. I had no way, and my friends suggested the military. So I enlisted in the military just to find myself. After being in the military, that might be what you want to do, or get an education, but it instills patriotism in you. The fact that you want to serve your country and the result of that willingness is that you may end up in a war or you may end up dead. I would like to think I am a true patriot because of the time I spent in the military. You don't have to be in the military to be a patriot, but it made my patriotism greater. All the other veterans should be thanking us.

USED WITH PERMISSION FROM THE KOREAN WAR LEGACY PROJECT

# Supporting Question 3

Source C: Everett Kelley, transcript of oral interview for Korean War Digital History Project (excerpt).

**Interviewer**: So, you had no prior knowledge, really, of what had happened between 1950 and 1953 [in Korea]?

**Everett Kelley**: I knew that there was a war, but... go ahead.

**Interviewer**: When or how did you learn more about the Korean War?

**EK**: Mainly through history, TV—things of that nature.

**Interviewer**: Did they teach you about it in school, when you were growing up and before your enlistment? Were they teaching it in schools yet?

**EK**: Well, they weren't teaching it, they were more teaching World War I and World War II back then. The Korean War was a recent event, it happened in the '50s and I was in school. I think I was in like the first grade in the '50s.

**Interviewer**: Do you have any messages for younger generations? Do you feel it's important for younger generations to know the sacrifices and contributions made in Korea [during the war]?

**EK**: I think that there were sacrifices of many soldiers who are traumatized and still suffering today from that war, and from all the other wars before [the Korean War].

**Interviewer**: Do you think it's important and necessary for us to preserve the interviews of these veterans and their legacy?

**EK**: Very important. Yes, I do.

**Interviewer**: And why do you think, in your opinion, the Korean War is known as the forgotten war?

**EK**: Well, it was after the big one: World War II, and a lot of soldiers that came out of Korea never got the benefits or the just treatment that they should've gotten from being what they called at that time "battle shocked" or "battle fatigued." I think the military environment is a great environment, a great experience, and I would think that every American should [...] experience it. But it is a traumatic experience when you have to go places and experience different cultures.

**Interviewer**: Is there anything else, any other stories or memories, messages that you had during your stay or anything else you would like to share to preserve your legacy?

**EK**: I think Korea is a great place. I don't regret one moment of my time in Korea. I gained a lot of insight that I would never have received had I not experienced that.

USED WITH PERMISSION FROM THE KOREAN WAR LEGACY PROJECT

# CHAPTER 15

# What Has Korea Meant to the United States?

Thomas Clouse and Kathy Swan

# WHAT HAS KOREA MEANT TO THE UNITED STATES?

| C3 Framework Indicator | **D2.His.1.9-12**. Evaluate how historical events and developments were shaped by unique circumstances of time and place as well as broader historical contexts. |
| --- | --- |
| Staging the Compelling Question | Watch the documentary from the Korean War Legacy Project and take notes about the types of relationships that it highlights. Use these notes to engage in a whole-class conversation about the personal and political relationships that have been forged between Korea and the U.S. since 1945. |

| SUPPORTING QUESTION 1 | SUPPORTING QUESTION 2 | SUPPORTING QUESTION 3 |
| --- | --- | --- |
| What did the Republic of Korea mean to the U.S. during the U.S. occupation? | How did the relationship between the U.S. and the Republic of Korea change during the Korean conflict? | What has the Republic of Korea meant to the U.S since the Korean conflict? |
| **FORMATIVE PERFORMANCE TASK** | **FORMATIVE PERFORMANCE TASK** | **FORMATIVE PERFORMANCE TASK** |
| List two reasons the U.S. occupied Korea, and cite evidence from the sources to support your reasoning. | Write one to two paragraphs that answer Supporting Question 2 using evidence from the sources. | Construct a claim using evidence to answer Supporting Question 3. |
| **FEATURED SOURCES** | **FEATURED SOURCES** | **FEATURED SOURCES** |
| **Source A:** Memo from Dean Acheson to Harry S. Truman, September 14, 1945<br>**Source B:** War Department Incoming Classified Message, September 18, 1945<br>**Source C:** Central Intelligence Group, "The Situation in Korea" (excerpt), Office of Reports and Estimates 5, January 3, 1947<br>**Source D:** Correspondence from George C. Marshall to Kenneth Royall, June 23, 1948<br>**Source E:** "The Position of the United States with Respect to Korea" (excerpt), *National Security Council Report*, March 16, 1949 | **Source A:** "The Truth about Korea," ca. 1950 (excerpt)<br>**Source B:** U.S. Department of State, Memorandum of Conversation on Korea, June 26, 1950<br>**Source C:** Oral history (excerpt) from Richard Hilton, Korean War Legacy Project (KWLP)<br>**Source D:** Oral history (excerpt) from Earl A. House (KWLP)<br>**Source E:** Summary examining the United States' role in involving the UN in the Korean War, United States Forces Korea (website)<br>**Source F:** Note by the White House Staff Secretary about President Dwight D. Eisenhower's policy toward Korea post-armistice, January, 5, 1954 | **Source A:** "Mutual Defense Treaty Between the United States and the Republic of Korea," October 1, 1953<br>**Source B:** Oral history (excerpt) from George H. Campbell, KWLP<br>**Source C:** Oral history (excerpt) from former congressional representative Charles Rangel (KWLP)<br>**Source D:** "Allies for 67 Years, U.S. and South Korea Split Over North Korea," *The New York Times*, September 4, 2017 |

| Summative Performance Task | **ARGUMENT** What has Korea meant to the United States? Construct an argument (e.g., detailed outline, poster, or essay) that discusses the compelling question using specific claims and relevant evidence from historical and contemporary sources while acknowledging competing views. |
| --- | --- |
| | **EXTENSION** Develop an annotated timeline that charts the relationship between the Republic of Korea and the United States since 1945. |
| Taking Informed Action | **UNDERSTAND** Research how many U.S. troops and military bases are on the Korean peninsula today and the current issues that challenge the U.S.-Republic of Korea alliance. |
| | **ASSESS** Write a list of pros and cons concerning the U.S. military presence in the Republic of Korea, noting whether this ongoing relationship remains worthwhile for both countries. |
| | **ACT** Create a position statement arguing for or against keeping U.S. troops in the Republic of Korea and post the statement to the Asia Unbound blog, which is part of the Council on Foreign Relations Network. |

# Overview
## Inquiry Description

This inquiry leads students through an investigation into the relationship between the United States and the Republic of Korea. By investigating the compelling question about what Korea means to the United States, students will have to consider the ways in which government documents and oral histories provide a unique way to understand this strategic relationship and make a claim on the significance of the Korean peninsula to the United States military.

This inquiry is expected to take four to seven 55-minute class periods. The inquiry time frame could expand if teachers think their students need additional instructional experiences (e.g., supporting questions, formative tasks, sources). Inquiries are not scripts, and teachers are encouraged to modify and adapt them in order to meet the requirements and interests of their particular students. Resources can also be modified as necessary to meet individualized education programs (IEPs) or Section 504 plans for students with disabilities.

## Structure of the Inquiry

In addressing the compelling question "What has Korea meant to the United States?" students will work through a series of supporting questions, performance tasks, and sources in order to construct an argument with evidence and counterevidence from a variety of sources.

### STAGING THE COMPELLING QUESTION

To begin this inquiry, students watch a documentary from the Korean War Legacy Project. The focus of the documentary is a Korean War veteran revisiting Korea with his great-grandson. As students view the video, they should be prompted to take notes on the types of relationships highlighted in the documentary. After the video, students will use these notes to engage in a whole-class conversation about the personal and political relationships that have been forged between the Republic of Korea and the United States since 1945.

### SUPPORTING QUESTION 1

The first supporting question is "What did Korea mean to the United States during the U.S. occupation?" It helps students to establish a foundational knowledge of the United States' purpose in Korea after the Japanese had been defeated and World War II ended. The formative performance task calls on students to use primary source documents to list the two main reasons behind the U.S. occupation of Korea, and give evidence to support each reason. The featured sources for this supporting question are a collection of government documents and correspondence from the Truman administration; these are sequenced chronologically. Featured Source A is a 1945 memo from State Department Undersecretary Dean Acheson to President Harry S. Truman. Acheson's memo details the situation in the Republic of Korea (South Korea) and includes as an attachment a recommended statement for Truman to make based on Acheson's understanding of the situation. Featured Source B is a then-classified War Department message from 1947 explaining the situation on the Korean peninsula. Featured Source C is a 1947 report on the situation in the Republic of Korea and the development of a self-sufficient government by U.S. occupying forces. Featured Source D is a letter sent in 1948 from the Secretary of State G. C. Marshall to the Secretary of the

Army, Kenneth Royall. The letter underlies the U.S. decision to begin to pull forces out of Korea. Teachers will want students to dwell in the space that this document creates as they work on the question "How does the fact that the U.S. was pulling out troops in 1948 answer what Korea meant to the U.S.?" Featured Source E is a declassified National Security Council report from 1949 that highlighted the situation in Korea as well as an assessment of the progress that had been made under the watch of the U.S. government.

## SUPPORTING QUESTION 2

For the second supporting question "How did the relationship between the U.S. and the Republic of Korea change during the Korean conflict?" students build on their understanding of Korea's importance to the United States government by analyzing key government correspondence as well as oral histories from Korean War veterans. Students will work to synthesize the information from the featured sources and write one to two paragraphs that answer this supporting question. Featured Source A is a government paper (circa 1950), "The Truth about Korea," which is a plea for bipartisan action at the domestic level, and restates the meaning and importance of Korea to the United States on an international level. Featured Source B is a memorandum of a conversation between President Truman, State Department officials, and U.S. military leadership about the "Korean Situation" after the Democratic Peoples' Republic of Korea (North Korea) invaded the Republic of Korea (South Korea). Featured Sources C and D are oral history excerpts from two veterans who recount what the relationship between the United States and the Republic of Korea meant during the conflict. Featured Source E is a summary of the United Nations Command's service in the Korean Conflict. Students should be encouraged to think about the role the United States played in getting the United Nations involved, as well as the amount of support the United States gave as a member of the United Nations. Featured Source F is a note by L. Arthur Minnich, the White House Staff Secretary, describing a statement by President Dwight D. Eisenhower in January 1954 about the continued U.S. commitment to the Republic of Korea even after the armistice that ended the war was signed.

## SUPPORTING QUESTION 3

Having examined the relationship between the Republic of Korea and the United States after World War II as well as during the Korean War, students will now be asked to answer the supporting question, "What has the Republic of Korea meant to the United States since the Korean conflict?" The formative task asks students to answer the supporting question by drawing on the featured sources to build and support a claim. Featured Source A is the mutual defense treaty signed by the United States and the Republic of Korea on October 1, 1953; this formal agreement details the military relationship between the two nations after the Korean War. Featured Sources B and C are excerpts of oral histories from two veterans who served in Korea. In each, the veterans describe the importance of the relationship between the Republic of Korea and the United States. Teachers will want to point out that the veteran in Featured Source C is former congressman Charles Rangel from New York. Featured Source D is a *New York Times* article describing the strong relationship that has existed between the United States and the Republic of Korea for the last 67 years, and outlining how rising tension with North Korea is complicating this longstanding alliance.

## SUMMATIVE PERFORMANCE TASK

In this task, students construct an evidence-based argument using multiple sources to answer the compelling question, "What has Korea meant to the United States?" Students' arguments could take a variety of forms, including a detailed outline, poster, or essay.

Students' arguments will vary, but could include any of the following:

- The meaning of the relationship between the United States and Korea has evolved over the last 80 years. Though initially about removing Japanese imperialism and reunifying the country, the relationship changed to be more about limiting the spread of communism, and later to preventing war on the peninsula.

- The relationship between the United States and Korea has been about stabilizing, but not reunifying, the peninsula. Though there were initial efforts to reunify North and South Korea, the relationship has more recently revolved around preventing communism and armed conflict from engulfing the region.

- The relationship between the United States and Korea has been mostly about protecting South Korea from outside influences. The U.S. military's involvement has centered around eliminating outside threats (e.g., Japanese imperialism and communism) in order to facilitate the establishment of a democratic government and ensuring economic security.

Students could extend the arguments by developing an annotated timeline charting the relationship between the Republic of Korea and the United States since 1945. Teachers will want to make sure that students not only chart the primary source documents that are the basis of this inquiry, but also examine important events that took place during the Korean War. The Korean War Legacy Project website provides valuable additional sources to examine as students develop their annotated timelines.

Students have the opportunity to take informed action by examining what Korea means to the United States today. To understand, students can research how many U.S. military personnel and bases are on the Korean peninsula today and the current issues that challenge the alliance between the two countries. To assess the issue, students could write a list of pros and cons concerning the U.S. military presence in the Republic of Korea, noting whether the ongoing relationship between the United States and the Republic of Korea remains worthwhile for both countries. To act, students could create a position statement arguing for or against keeping U.S. troops in the Republic of Korea, and then post their statements on the Asia Unbound blog maintained by the Council on Foreign Relations that examines the United States' involvement in Asia.

# Staging the Compelling Question

**FEATURED SOURCE**     Source: Sultan Sharrief, "The Legacy: A Documentary," Korean War Legacy Project.

https://koreanwarlegacy.org

This documentary features Arden Rowley, a Korean War veteran, as he visits South Korea with his great grandson, Cayden Sherwood, to remember his wartime experiences and see the dramatic development of the country since the war. Students can reflect on the different kinds of relationships portrayed in the documentary.

# Supporting Question 1

Source A: Memo from Acting Secretary of State Dean Acheson to President Harry S. Truman suggesting a public statement clarifying the United States' intentions regarding Japanese officials stationed in Korea upon the occupation of the Korean capital by the U.S. Armed Forces, September 14, 1945.

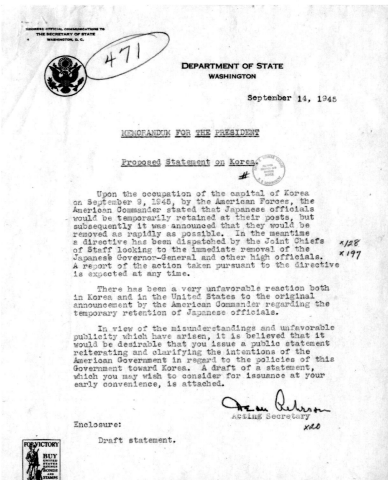

**DEPARTMENT OF STATE**
WASHINGTON

September 14, 1945

MEMORANDUM FOR THE PRESIDENT

Proposed Statement on Korea.

Upon the occupation of the capital of Korea on September 9, 1945, by the American Forces, the American Commander stated that Japanese officials would be temporarily retained at their posts, but subsequently it was announced that they would be removed as rapidly as possible. In the meantime a directive has been dispatched by the Joint Chiefs of Staff looking to the immediate removal of the Japanese Governor-General and other high officials. A report of the action taken pursuant to the directive is expected at any time.

There has been a very unfavorable reaction both in Korea and in the United States to the original announcement by the American Commander regarding the temporary retention of Japanese officials.

In view of the misunderstandings and unfavorable publicity which have arisen, it is believed that it would be desirable that you issue a public statement reiterating and clarifying the intentions of the American Government in regard to the policies of this Government toward Korea. A draft of a statement, which you may wish to consider for issuance at your early convenience, is attached.

Acting Secretary

Enclosure:

Draft statement.

STATEMENT BY THE PRESIDENT

Draft

The surrender of the Japanese forces in Seoul, ancient Korean capital, heralds the liberation of a freedom-loving and heroic people. Despite their long and cruel subjection under the warlords of Japan, the Koreans have kept alive their devotion to national liberty and to their proud cultural heritage. This subjection has now ended. The Japanese warlords are being removed. Such Japanese as may be temporarily retained are being utilized as servants of the Korean people and of our occupying forces only because they are deemed essential by reason of their technical qualifications.

In this moment of liberation we are mindful of the difficult tasks which lie ahead. The building of a great nation has now begun with the assistance of the United States, China, Great Britain and the Soviet Union, who are agreed that Korea shall become free and independent.

The assumption by the Koreans themselves of the responsibilities and functions of a free and independent nation and the elimination of all vestiges of Japanese control over Korean economic and political life will of necessity require time and patience. The goal is in view but its speedy attainment will require the joint efforts of the Korean people and of the allies.

The

- 2 -

The American people rejoice in the liberation of Korea as the Tae-gook-kee, the ancient flag of Korea, waves again in the Land of the Morning Calm.

# Supporting Question 1

Source B: Incoming Classified Message to the War Department describing "the general situation" in South Korea as "a powder keg ready to explode," September 18, 1945.

http://www.trumanlibrary.org/whistlestop/study_collections/koreanwar/index.php

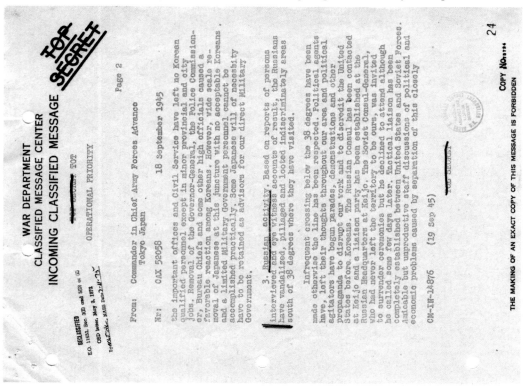

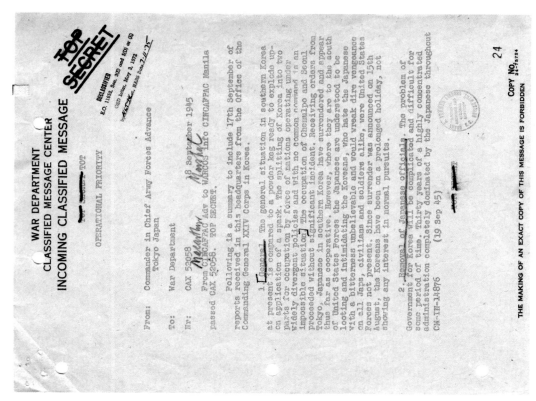

WAR DEPARTMENT
CLASSIFIED MESSAGE CENTER
INCOMING CLASSIFIED MESSAGE

DECLASSIFIED
E.O. 11652, Sec. 3(E) and 5(D) or (E)
OSD letter, May 3, 1972
By _____ NARS Date 7-11-__

NOT SECRET TOT    OPERATIONAL PRIORITY

Page 3

From: Commander in Chief Army Forces Advance
Tokyo Japan

Nr:    CAX 52058    18 September 1945

integrated country have taken place. The Koreans themselves have for so long a time been down-trodden that they cannot now or in the immediate future have a rational acceptance of this situation and its responsibilities. There has been a misconception also as to how immediate their independence is to be and as to how quickly the Japs will be thrown out. Already political parties with so called leaders are being born in emotion. Some are Communist and others support the Chungking Provisional Government. G-2 is investigating many political parties which have recently mushroomed. However, manifestations indicate the possible desirability of bringing in the Provisional Government and such persons as Kim Koo and Syngman Rhee and others of his group. Some older and more educated Koreans despite being now suspected of collaboration are conservatives and may develop into quite useful groups.

5. Personnel. The XXIV Corps is small in strength and short of competent staff and Military Government personnel which forces operations in limited areas and hence with little overall effect. Necessity for expanding throughout all Provinces in our area is urgent. The American troops have not yet been required to fire a shot or to injure an inhabitant and they have restored and maintained order wherever they have gone: both facts are significant of their prestige.

6. Monetary matters. The Korean Monetary System has been thoroughly sabotaged and it will be impossible to

CM-IN-14876    (19 Sep 45)

TOP SECRET

24

COPY NO.
24-78724

THE MAKING OF AN EXACT COPY OF THIS MESSAGE IS FORBIDDEN

---

WAR DEPARTMENT
CLASSIFIED MESSAGE CENTER
INCOMING CLASSIFIED MESSAGE

DECLASSIFIED
E.O. 11652, Sec. 3(E) and 5(D) or (E)
OSD letter, May 3, 1972
By _____ NARS Date 7-11-__

NOT SECRET TOT    OPERATIONAL PRIORITY

Page 4

From: Commander in Chief Army Forces Advance
Tokyo Japan

Nr:    CAX 52058    18 September 1945

enforce the pegging of prices at the 15th August levels.

Threatened by bank runs, the Japanese have issued several billions of yen of newly printed Bank of Chosen notes in the last few weeks resulting in the skyrocketing of wages and prices and a thriving black market. United States Forces have been ordered to refrain from all local purchases without permit but only the introduction of a complete new Monetary System can reestablish fiscal controls.

7. Foodstuff. Although there is a fairly adequate storehouse supply of foodstuff, distribution and rationing have broken down badly and successful reinstatement is not likely. Disruption of railways and lack of motor transport impairs movement of foodstuffs. All assistance is being given in rehabilitating Jap Army transport, but railway situation most serious with only ten days fuel supply available, south Korean mines not producing and negotiations not concluded to obtain coal from north Korean mines in Russian Zone.

8. Industries. Hundreds of thousands are unemployed by collapse of war industries and strikes are threatened in railways and public utilities. A general work holiday is being staged by many identifying independence with freedom from work despite propaganda emphasis to stay on job and rebuild for Koreans. A situation ripe for agitation has developed and being further agravated by the lack of raw material and the location of coal and primary power sources in the Russian Zone.

CM-IN-14876    (19 Sep 45)

24

COPY NO.
24-78724

THE MAKING OF AN EXACT COPY OF THIS MESSAGE IS FORBIDDEN

**TOP SECRET**

WAR DEPARTMENT
CLASSIFIED MESSAGE CENTER
INCOMING CLASSIFIED MESSAGE

DECLASSIFIED
E.O. 11652, Sec. 3(E) and 5(D) or (E)
OSD letter, May 3, 1972
By _____ NARS Date _____

TOT         OPERATIONAL PRIORITY

Page 6

From:   Commander in Chief Army Forces Advance
        Tokyo Japan

Nr:     CAX 52058        18 September 1945

all functions immediately. Before they got any glimmer of
conditions as they existed, they were highly critical of all
policies of the Nation, of General Headquarters and of this
headquarters relating to the occupation. This latter con-
dition is now rectifying itself slowly as they begin to see
the picture. One group arrived by air one afternoon, filed
stories that evening and left the next morning, feeling
that they knew all about the Korean occupation.

                                        End.

ACTION :  Gen Hull

INFO   :  JC/S
          Adm Leahy
          Gen Arnold
          Gen Somervell
          OPD (for State Dept)
          Gen Bissell
          Gen Hilldring
          Adm King
          Gen Surles
          Gen Richards
          Mr McCloy
          C of S

CM-IN-14876    (19 Sep 45)    DTG 181601Z    hcw

**TOP SECRET**

24

---

**TOP SECRET**

WAR DEPARTMENT
CLASSIFIED MESSAGE CENTER
INCOMING CLASSIFIED MESSAGE

DECLASSIFIED
E.O. 11652, Sec. 3(E) and 5(D) or (E)
OSD letter, May 3, 1972
By _____ NARS Date _____

TOT         OPERATIONAL PRIORITY

Page 5

From:   Commander in Chief Army Forces Advance
        Tokyo Japan

Nr:     CAX 52058        18 September 1945

9. Demobilization  Nothing approaching stable
conditions in Korea can be established until the Japanese
Army and most of the Japanese population have been removed
to Japan. Demobilization of the Japanese Army in Korea is
absolutely impossible. It will have to be kept in formed
bodies and removed to Japan beginning as soon as its dis-
armament is complete. It will be a source of irritation as
long as in Korea. It cannot be controlled here unless taken
over and put in guarded cages where we have to feed, house and
care for them. Ferries are now operating from Fusen to
Kyushu capable of transporting about 6,000 to 7,000 individuals per day. They are carrying Japanese to Japan and
Koreans to Korea at about equal rate. It is believed that
these should be continued since nationals of the two nations
are piling up in the ports on each side of the channel trying to get home and the exchange does not affect the balance
of individuals to be fed and housed but does reduce the
capacity in each area for making trouble. However, it would
greatly assist the occupation to transport the Japanese Army
home at an early date, supervising this move at the port.

10. The Press  The newspaper correspondents covering
Korea as a group have behaved badly. They arrived by air
after our landing, most of them from Japan with no knowledge of the local situation and without orientation took
advantage of the American uniform to run rampant over the
area, committing acts of personal misbehavior that troops
have been forbidden to do. There is reason to believe that
by open sympathies with Korean radicals some of them have
incited Korean group leaders to greater efforts at agitation
for overthrow of everything and to have the Koreans take over

CM-IN-14876    (19 Sep 45)

**TOP SECRET**

24

Source C: Central Intelligence Group report on "The Situation in Korea" (excerpt), Office of Reports and Estimates 5, January 3, 1947.

http://www.trumanlibrary.org/whistlestop/study_collections/koreanwar/index.php

ORE 5/1

3 January 1947

Copy No. 1

### CENTRAL INTELLIGENCE GROUP

### THE SITUATION IN KOREA

#### SUMMARY

Unity and independence are the dominant aspirations of the Korean people, while partition and joint occupation by the US and USSR are the governing factors in the political and economic life of the peninsula. The promises of independence made at Cairo, and confirmed at Yalta, have not been fulfilled. The division of Korea at the 38th parallel has become an almost impenetrable barrier between the US and Soviet Zones. The Moscow Decision, which provides for the unification and eventual independence of Korea, has not been implemented, largely because of disagreement between the US and USSR over the interpretation of the document and the meaning of democracy. All efforts to reconvene the Joint Commission since its adjournment last May have failed.

In the current deadlock, both the US and USSR are attempting to strengthen the political and economic organization of their own zones. The USSR has made more rapid progress toward regimentation in North Korea than the US has made toward democracy in its zone. An interim US policy for South Korea was not implemented until after the adjournment of the Joint Commission disclosed the fundamental disagreement over interpretation of the Moscow Decision. The sovietization of North Korea, on the other hand, began immediately after the occupation, and has proceeded without interruption since then.

Soviet policy in Korea is directed toward the establishment of a friendly state which will never serve as a base of attack upon the USSR. In order to attain this objective at a minimum cost to its own scanty resources in the Far East, the USSR has attempted to make North Korea economically self-sufficient though politically subordinate. Soviets have given their zone a semblance of autonomy by entrusting the administration to a hierarchy of "people's committees" dominated by the Korean Communists. The economy of North Korea has also been reconstructed on the principle of state control. Banking, heavy industry and communications have all been nationalized. The land has been redistributed, and private enterprise survives chiefly in agriculture and handicrafts. Membership is compulsory in a monopolistic system of unions under strict political supervision.

FEATURED SOURCE    Source D: Correspondence from George C. Marshall to Kenneth Royall, following up on "The Position of the United States with Respect to Korea," June 23, 1948.

http://www.trumanlibrary.org/whistlestop/study_collections/koreanwar/index.php

COPY                              TOP SECRET

June 23, 1948

Dear Mr. Secretary:

It will be recalled that on April 8, 1948, the President approved the Conclusions of National Security Council paper No. 8 on The Position of the United States with Respect to Korea, and directed that they be implemented by all appropriate Executive Departments and Agencies of this Government under my coordination.

It is my understanding that the Department of the Army, in accordance with the foregoing directive, has authorized the initiation of preparations for the withdrawal of occupation forces from Korea, and that, for planning purposes, August 15, 1948 has been set as the date on which actual troop withdrawal will commence. These preparatory measures would appear to be entirely consistent with the provision of the National Security Council paper that "every effort should be made to create conditions for the withdrawal of occupation forces by 31 December 1948."

In the light of the present world political situation, however, and of the inescapable effect which our actions in Korea will have upon that situation, it is of particular importance that withdrawal should be "phased in consonance with the accomplishment of the objectives outlined /in that paper/ and with the relevant commitments of the U.S. vis-a-vis the UN". While every effort should be made to bring about the withdrawal of our occupation forces from Korea by the end of the current year as presently contemplated, sufficient flexibility should be maintained in the preparation and execution of withdrawal plans to make possible changes in the implementation of such plans which UN action or other developments may make advisable.

I assume, therefore, that the plans of the Department of the Army for withdrawal of our occupation forces from Korea, and particularly before initiation of actual withdrawal, are adaptable to changes which may be necessary to correlate with developments contemplated in the National Security Council paper. Assistant Secretary Saltzman will act as my representative in connection with the implementation of the National Security Council paper.

Faithfully yours,

G. C. Marshall

The Honorable
    Kenneth C. Royall,
        Secretary of the Army.

TOP SECRET

FEATURED SOURCE

Source E: National Security Council report, "The Position of the United States with Respect to Korea" (excerpts, drafts of pages 1, 17, 18 and 19), March 16, 1949.

http://www.trumanlibrary.org/whistlestop/study_collections/koreanwar

D R A F T

REPORT BY THE NATIONAL SECURITY COUNCIL

on

THE POSITION OF THE UNITED STATES WITH RESPECT TO KOREA

THE PROBLEM

1. To re-assess and re-appraise the position of the U. S. with respect to Korea as defined in NSC 8 of April 2, 1948, in the light of developments since the adoption of that position.

ANALYSIS

2. a. Objectives of U. S. policy in Korea as defined by NSC 8:

(1) The broad objectives of U. S. policy with respect to Korea are:

(a) to establish a united, self-governing, and sovereign Korea as soon as possible, independent of foreign control and eligible for membership in the UN;

(b) to ensure that the government so established shall be fully representative of the freely expressed will of the Korean people;

(c) to assist the Korean people in establishing a sound economy and educational system as essential bases of an independent and democratic state.

A more immediate objective is the withdrawal of

- 1 -

NSC 8/1

CONCLUSIONS

3. It is concluded that:

a. The broad objectives of the U. S. with respect to Korea should continue to be those set forth in paragraph 2-a above.

b. In pursuance of those objectives the U. S. should continue to give political support and economic, technical, military, and other assistance to the Government of the Republic of Korea.

c. Preparation should be made for the withdrawal of remaining U. S. occupation forces from Korea, such withdrawal to be completed on or about June 30, 1949, subject to consultation with the UN Commission on Korea and the Korean Government and assuming the completion by that date of the transfer of military equipment and supplies in accordance with paragraph 3-d below.

d. Prior to the final withdrawal of such U. S. forces there should be transferred to the Government of the Republic of Korea for its security forces at least a six-months stockpile of military equipment and supplies, with combat reserve, based on a Korean Army strength of 65,000 men.

e. There should be established in Korea forthwith a U. S. military advisory group, already in existence on a provisional basis, which will be responsible for the effective training of the Korean Army, coast guard (Navy), and Police, and for the effective utilization of U. S. military assistance by these forces.

- 17 -

NSC 8/1

i.  The U. S. should seek to promote sympathetic interest and participation in the Korean problem and support of the Government of the Republic of Korea by the UN and by its individual member states, and should continue to cooperate with the UN in the solution of that problem. In particular, the U. S. should lend all appropriate support to the efforts of the UN Commission on Korea established under the GA Resolution of December 12 in its efforts to help the Korean people and their lawful Government to achieve the goal of a free and united Korea.

k.  In publicly announcing the withdrawal of its remaining occupation forces from Korea, the U. S. should make it unmistakably clear that this step in no way constitutes a lessening of U. S. support of the Government of the Republic of Korea, but constitutes rather another step toward the regularization by the U. S. of its relations with that Government and a fulfillment on the part of the U. S. of the relevant provision of the GA Resolution of December 12, 1948.

f.  Legislative authorization should be sought for continuing military assistance to the Government of the Republic of Korea for FY 1950, and thereafter subject to developments, designed to provide that government with:

(1) a well-trained and -equipped Army of at least 65,000 men, capable of maintaining internal order under conditions of political strife and inspired disorder and of assuring border security;

(2) a well-trained and -equipped coast guard (Navy) capable of assuring to a reasonable degree the security of the port facilities and coast lines of south Korea;

(3) a well-trained and -equipped police force capable of performing the normal police functions of law enforcement and of cooperating when necessary with the Army in the preservation of public order.

g.  Legislative authorization should also be sought for the presently contemplated ECA program for Korea for FY 1950 and, subject to annual review in the light of developments, for the continuance of economic and technical assistance to Korea beyond FY 1950.

h.  An effort should be made to increase the effectiveness of the informational, cultural, educational, and exchange of persons programs in Korea in accordance with the peculiar requirements of the situation existing in that country.

i.  All phases of U. S. Government activity in Korea should be unified in a combined American Mission in Korea under the over-all direction of the American Ambassador.

NSC 8/1

- 18 -

Source A: Unknown author, "The Truth about Korea," ca. 1950 (excerpt).

http://www.trumanlibrary.org/whistlestop/study_collections/koreanwar

## FOREWORD

The unprovoked aggression by the Soviet dominated government of North Korea against the Republic of Korea has created widespread interest in recent relations of the United States with Korea. There have been full accounts of U.S.-Korean relations published recently by the Department of State and Congressional committees. In order, however, that the most significant facts may be readily available, they are set out in this pamphlet.

President Truman, the Democratic Party and the Democratic leadership and membership in the Senate and House of Representatives believe firmly that foreign affairs should be conducted on a bipartisan or non-partisan basis. That is undoubtedly the belief of a farsighted but comparatively small group in the Republican party and in the Republican membership in the Senate and House. Full tribute is paid here and now to the wisdom and patriotism of these men and women.

There can be no question, however, that the leadership of the Republican party and its leadership and the majority of its membership in the Senate and House, motivated by isolationism and pure partisanship, have endeavored in many cases to obstruct the adoption of foreign policy measures vital to the welfare of the country which have been advanced by the Administration and in fact supported on a bipartisan basis by farsighted Republicans.

These Republican leaders in the party and the Congress are now engaged in a frenzied effort to hide their guilt for obstructing the efforts of the Administration to strengthen the Republic of Korea and the free world. They are brazenly propagating false and distorted accounts of certain aspects of U.S.-Korean relations. These matters are dealt with particularly to make certain the truth is known.

*[This foreword is the second page of the document, which continues on pages 202-203.]*

# THE SIGNIFICANCE OF KOREA

Korea is a mountainous peninsula slightly larger than New England, New Jersey and Maryland combined. It has a total population of about 30 million. The Republic of Korea south of the 38th parallel embraces about half of the land area and 20 million of the people. Korea had been annexed by Japan in 1910 and remained a Japanese colony until liberated at the end of World War II.

The significance of Korea cannot be measured in terms of its relatively small area and population. In the great world struggle in which the United States and other free nations are resisting the determined efforts of the Soviet imperialism to dominate the world, the success of American efforts to help the people of Korea build a free nation is of immeasurable importance. As President Truman said in proposing the "little ECA" for Korea to the Congress on June 7, 1949:

"Korea has become a testing ground in which the validity and practical value of the ideals and principles of democracy which the Republic is putting into practice are being matched against the practices of communism which have been imposed on the people of North Korea. The survival and progress of the Republic of Korea toward a self-supporting, stable economy will have an immense and far-reaching influence on the people of Asia. Moreover, the Korean Republic, by demonstrating the success and tenacity of democracy in resisting communism, will stand as a beacon on the people of northern Asia in resisting the control of communist forces which have overrun them.

"If we are faithful to our ideals and mindful of our interests in establishing peaceful and prosperous conditions in the world, we will not fail to provide the aid which is so essential to Korea at this critical time."

## Background of Policy

The question of policy toward Korea was first discussed by the Allies during the war at the Cairo Conference of December 1943. At that time the United States, the United Kingdom and China were looking for means to create dissension within the Japanese Empire and help split it up. They also had in mind the long-range purposes of the war against Japan.

They recognized the enslavement of the people of Korea and stated their determination that "in due course Korea shall become free and independent."

Later on at Potsdam they agreed that the terms of the Cairo declaration should be carried out. When Soviet Russia declared war on Japan on August 8, 1945, it also joined in the Potsdam declaration and thus committed itself to the freedom and independence of Korea.

# The 38th Parallel

Among the many oft-repeated false statements of partisan propagandists are those that the United States gave Korea north of the 38th parallel to Russia at Yalta, and that the Administration was at fault in not occupying all of Korea. As usual, the facts are quite different. There are three which are most important:

(1) Neither the division of Korea along the 38th parallel nor the joint occupation of Korea was decided upon or in fact considered in any way at the Yalta or Potsdam Conferences. It was not the subject of any agreement, secret or otherwise.

(2) The drawing of the line was entirely a military decision recommended by Secretary Stimson upon the advice of the Joint Chiefs of Staff.

The sole purpose of the line was to define the areas in which United States forces and Soviet forces would accept the surrender of Japanese troops in Korea at the end of the war against Japan. When the question was being considered on August 11-15, 1945, Soviet forces already were well into Manchuria. Other Soviet forces were on the border between Korea and the Soviet Maritime Provinces. Some had already entered Korea. The great Soviet base of Vladivostok is only some eighty miles from the northeast border of Korea. On the other hand, the nearest American forces were on Okinawa, some 600 miles south of Korea, and were needed to occupy Japan while most of the forces available for movement into Korea were as far distant as the Philippines, some 1500 to 2000 miles away.

It was recognized by the military and foreign policy authorities that the line should be drawn as far north as it was practicable for our troops to reach. The military authorities with the advice of the Joint Chiefs of Staff recommended the 38th parallel because it included the Korean capital of Seoul with its port and communication area and because under the circumstances at the time the United States could not send to Korea the forces necessary to receive the Japanese surrender further north.

Secretary Stimson submitted this recommendation to the State-War-Navy Coordinating Committee and it was included in General Order No. 1.

This was issued by General MacArthur as Supreme Commander for the Allied Powers to the Japanese Government for all of the Japanese armed forces.

(3) Far from permitting the Soviet Union to take over a part of Korea from which it could have been excluded, the establishment of the 38th parallel line actually held for the free people of Korea the southern half of the country, which otherwise would easily have been overrun by the Red Army.

## 5

## United States Efforts to Unite Korea

It should, of course, be thoroughly understood that the division of Korea and the movement of United States forces into Korea was never intended to be for a long-term occupation. This was a development which resulted from the persistent refusal of the USSR to agree to the establishment of a united and independent Korea upon terms which would do justice to the aspirations of the Korean people for freedom and national independence.

At the Cairo Conference, in December 1943, the United States, Great Britain and China had declared that, after Japan had been defeated, all Korea would become a single Republic. This was reaffirmed at the Potsdam Conference, in July 1945. The Soviets joined in that pledge. From the first days after the acceptance of Japanese surrender, the United States endeavored to obtain agreement of fulfillment by the USSR of its pledge. The Soviets on their part refused to deal with any non-Communist Korean groups and rejected every reasonable proposal advanced. At the same time, they engaged in an ever-increasing campaign of anti-American propaganda and vilification and commenced to create Communist controlled military forces in North Korea. In view of this stalemate, it was concluded that the justified desire of the Korean people for independence and unity entitled them to have the aid of the world community in getting it. Therefore, the United States took the Korean problem to the United Nations in November of 1947, asking that Korea be established as a unified nation through election of a provisional government which would draw up a constitution. The Korean issue was handled before the General Assembly by Mr. John Foster Dulles, a member of the U. S. Delegation. The proposal was approved by a vote of 43-0, with Russia and her satellites abstaining.

The election was observed by a United Nations Commission but was confined to south Korea because the puppet communist officials of North Korea refused to let the United Nations Commission travel north of the 38th parallel. More than 95% of the eligible voters of South Korea participated in the election in spite of communist terrorism that left nearly 100 Koreans dead during the election.

The National Assembly of the democratic Republic of Korea adopted its constitution on July 12, 1948. The constitution promised the Korean people "security, liberty, and happiness" and provided for democratic government. This constitution only affected the two-thirds of the population living south of the 38th parallel. One hundred seats in the legislature of the Republic were left vacant for representatives of the people in Northern Korea. The Republic of Korea was inaugurated August 15, 1948.

Meanwhile, the Soviet controlled North Korean regime announced that a constitution for the "Korean Democratic People's Republic" had been adopted and that elections would be held in August of 1948 to elect representatives. The communist North Korean government pretended to hold a "nation-wide" election with "secret" ballots being cast in South Korea.

## 6

The General Assembly in September 1948 recognized the Republic of Korea as the only democratically established government in Korea. The United States and all the major free nations have recognized the Republic. The United States sponsored the admission of the Republic to the United Nations but Soviet Russia vetoed its entrance. (USSR and Ukranian delegates cast the only opposing votes.)

## Withdrawal of United States Forces

Partisan practitioners of hindsight are now claiming that the withdrawal of United States forces from Korea was an unsound step not advised by American military authorities and should not have been taken. They add that if American forces had been left, the north Korean attack would not have come.

The facts are: The withdrawal was primarily for military reasons and upon the recommendation of military authorities. It was requested by the United Nations. It was made upon the recommendation of and in full consultation with responsible Republican officials. It was made only after General MacArthur had stated that Korean security forces were prepared to take over.

In the first place, the withdrawal of American forces was primarily for military reasons and upon the recommendation of the Defense establishment. American military manpower was severely limited by the rapid demobilization demanded by the people at the end of the war, by the cut in funds available for military purposes made necessary by the Republican-sponsored Knutson tax bill and by the limitations on manpower for American armed forces.

It was therefore necessary for United States military authorities to spread our available manpower thin throughout the many areas of United States world-wide responsibility where potential danger might become real trouble.

Prior to the time the United States took the Korean case to the UN in the fall of 1947, the responsible authorities in the United States Government considered specifically whether the United States had any strategic reason for retaining forces there.

In light of the facts stated above, the Joint Chiefs of Staff stated, and the Secretary of Defense informed the State-War-Navy Coordinating Committee, that the United States had little strategic interest in maintaining the existing troops in Korea. At that time the Joint Chiefs of Staff were General Eisenhower, Admiral Nimitz and General Spaatz of the Air Force. The Secretary of Defense was Mr. Forrestal. They felt that existing shortages of military manpower in many areas of American responsibility throughout the world, made it essential that all available manpower be utilized in accordance with the relative military priorities of such areas.

Because of these military considerations the resolution on Korea submitted to the UN by the United States in October 1947 contained a provision calling for the withdrawal of all occupying forces.

FEATURED SOURCE    Source B: Department of State, Memorandum of Conversation, "Subject: Korean Situation," June 26, 1950.

http://www.trumanlibrary.org/whistlestop/study_collections/koreanwar

TOP SECRET

- 2 -

operations in Korea and to offer the fullest possible support to the South Korean forces, attacking tanks, guns, columns, etc., of the North Korean forces in order to give a chance to the South Koreans to reform.

THE PRESIDENT said he approved this.

MR. PACE inquired whether this meant action only south of the 38th parallel.

MR. ACHESON said this was correct. He was making no suggestion for any action across the line.

GENERAL VANDENBERG asked whether this meant also that they should not fly over the line.

MR. ACHESON said they should not.

THE PRESIDENT said this was correct; that no action should be taken north of the 38th parallel. He added "not yet".

MR. PACE said that care should be used to avoid hitting friendly forces.

GENERAL COLLINS agreed but suggested that the orders themselves should not put restrictions on the operation.

MR. ACHESON said that if it was considered useful the orders could add that the purpose which the orders would implement is to support South Korean forces in conformity with the resolution of the Security Council.

MR. ACHESON said that the second point he wished to bring up was that orders should be issued to the Seventh Fleet to prevent an attack on Formosa.

THE PRESIDENT said he agreed.

MR. ACHESON continued that at the same time the National Government of China should be told to desist from operations against the mainland and that the Seventh Fleet should be ordered to see that those operations would cease.

MR. ACHESON said his third point was an increase in the United States military forces in the Philippines and an acceleration

TOP SECRET

---

TOP SECRET
COPY NO. 1
OF 6 COPIES

DEPARTMENT OF STATE

TOP SECRET Memorandum of Conversation

DATE: June 26, 1950

LIMITED DISTRIBUTION

SUBJECT:    Korean Situation

PARTICIPANTS:    The President

Secretary Acheson
Secretary Johnson

Secretary Pace
Secretary Finletter
General Bradley
Admiral Sherman
General Vandenberg
General Collins

Mr. Matthews )
Mr. Rusk ) State
Mr. Hickerson ) Dept
Mr. Jessup )

(Secretary Matthews arrived just after meeting adjourned)

The above group met with the President at Blair House at 9:00 PM.

GENERAL VANDENBERG reported that the first Yak plane had been shot down.

THE PRESIDENT remarked that he hoped that it was not the last.

GENERAL VANDENBERG read the text of the orders which had been issued to our Air Forces calling on them to take "aggressive action" against any planes interfering with their mission or operating in a manner unfriendly to the South Korean forces. He indicated, however, that they had been avoiding combat where the direct carrying-out of their mission was not involved.

MR. ACHESON suggested that an all-out order be issued to the Navy and Air Force to waive all restrictions on their operations

TOP SECRET

- 3 -

acceleration of aid to the Philippines in order that we might have a firm base there.

THE PRESIDENT said he agreed.

MR. ACHESON said his fourth point was that aid to Indo-china should be stepped up and that a strong military mission should be sent.

He suggested that on all these matters if orders were issued tonight it would be desirable for the President to make a statement tomorrow. He handed the President a rough draft of the type of statement which might be issued.

THE PRESIDENT said he would work on the statement tonight. The President continued that he wished consideration given to taking Formosa back as part of Japan and putting it under MacArthur's Command.

MR. ACHESON said that he had considered this move but had felt that it should be reserved for later and should not be announced at this time. It required further study.

THE PRESIDENT said that he had a letter from the Generalissimo about one month (?) ago to the effect that the Generalissimo might step out of the situation if that would help. He said this was a private letter and he had kept it secret. He said that we might want to proceed along those lines in order to get Chinese forces helping us. He thought that the Generalissimo might step out if MacArthur were put in.

MR. ACHESON said that the Generalissimo was unpredictable and that it was possible that he might resist and "throw the ball game". He said that it might be well to do this later.

THE PRESIDENT said that that was alright. He himself thought that it was the next step.

MR. JOHNSON said that the proposals made by the Secretary of State pleased him very much. He thought that if we hold the line as indicated that that was alright.

MR. ACHESON added in regard to the Formosan situation that he thought it undesirable that we should get mixed up in the question of the Chinese administration of the Island.

THE

TOP SECRET

- 4 -

Chinese "a nickel" for any purpose whatever. He said that all the money we had given them is now invested in United States real estate.

MR. JOHNSON added or in banks in the Philippine Islands.

ADMIRAL SHERMAN said that the Command of the Seventh Fleet could be either under Admiral Radford at Pearl Harbor or under General MacArthur. He said that under the orders issued yesterday the Seventh Fleet had been ordered to proceed to Japan and placed under General MacArthur's Command. He said that the orders in regard to Formosa would be issued from the Joint Chiefs of Staff to General MacArthur so to employ the forces allocated by Admiral Radford to General MacArthur.

No objection was raised to this statement.

MR. ACHESON said that the Security Council would meet tomorrow afternoon and that the Department had prepared a further resolution for adoption. Our reports were that we would get full support. He noted that even the Swedes were now supporting us.

MR. HICKERSON read the draft of the Security Council resolution recommending that UN members render such assistance as was needed to Korea to repel the attack.

THE PRESIDENT said that was right. He said we wanted everyone in on this, including Hong Kong.

GENERAL BRADLEY reported that British Air Marshall Tedder had come in to see him, was generally in accord with our taking the firm position, and gave General Bradley a full report of the forces which the British have in that area.

MR. RUSK pointed out that it was possible the Russians would come to the Security Council meeting and cast a veto. In that case we would still take the position that we could act in support of the Charter.

THE PRESIDENT said that was right. He rather wished they would veto. He said we needed to lay a base for our action in Formosa. He said that he would work on the draft of his statement tonight and would talk to the Defense and State Departments in the morning regarding the final text.

MR. RUSK

TOP SECRET

THE PRESIDENT said that he had a meeting scheduled for 10:00 tomorrow morning with the Big Four and that he would get in any others that the Secretary thought should be added. He suggested that Secretaries Acheson and Johnson should also be there.

MR. JOHNSON suggested that the majority and minority members of the two Armed Services Committees be included.

After the discussion it was agreed to set the meeting for 11:30.

THE PRESIDENT then read the following list of persons to be included in the meeting:

> The Big Four (Lucas, Rayburn, McCormack - the Vice President will be out of town), Senators Connally, Wiley, George, Alexander Smith, Thomas of Utah, Tydings and Bridges; Congressmen Kee, Eaton, Vinson and Short.

MR. JOHNSON referred again to the draft statement for the President, said that it was very forthright, that he liked it very much and that the Joint Chiefs would consider it during the evening and make any suggestions in the morning.

GENERAL COLLINS stated that the military situation in Korea was bad. It was impossible to say how much our air can do. The Korean Chief of Staff has no fight left in him.

MR. ACHESON stated that it was important for us to do something even if the effort were not successful.

MR. JOHNSON said that even if we lose Korea this action would save the situation. He said this action "suits me". He then asked whether any of the military representatives had any objection to the course of action which had been outlined. There was no objection.

GENERAL VANDENBERG, in response to a question from Mr. Finletter, said that he bet a tank would be knocked out before dark.

THE

---

MR. RUSK pointed out that it was Mr. Kennan's estimate that Formosa would be the next likely spot for a Communist move.

SECRETARY JOHNSON reported that SCAP's guess was that the next move would be on Iran. He thought there should be a check on this.

GENERAL COLLINS said that SCAP did not have as much global information as they have in Washington. He and Mr. Pace stated that they have asked for full reports all over the world in regard to any developments, particularly of Soviet preparations.

SECRETARY JOHNSON suggested to Mr. Acheson that it would be advisable to have some talks with the UK regarding possible action in Iran.

MR. ACHESON said he would talk with both the British and French.

MR. ACHESON asked Admiral Sherman whether he desired that any action should be taken regarding the utilization of the Sakishimas, south of Okinawa.

ADMIRAL SHERMAN said he would leave this to General MacArthur.

MR. ACHESON said it would be better to put any necessary supporting air forces on these Islands than to try to put them on Formosa itself.

MR. PACE inquired whether the State Department would inform Ambassador Muccio concerning the orders which were being given.

MR. ACHESON said from latest reports it would probably be impossible for us to contact Ambassador Muccio.

GENERAL COLLINS reported that they were in contact with Seoul through a ham radio operator there.

MR. PACE said that they could pass a message to Ambassador Muccio through General MacArthur.

MR. ACHESON suggested that the President might wish to get in Senator Connally and other members of the Senate and House and tell them what had been decided.

THE

THE PRESIDENT said he had done everything he could for five years to prevent this kind of situation. Now the situation is here and we must do what we can to meet it. He had been wondering about the mobilization of the National Guard and asked General Bradley if that was necessary now. If it was he must go to Congress and ask for funds. He was merely putting the subject on the table for discussion. He repeated we must do everything we can for the Korean situation - "for the United Nations".

GENERAL BRADLEY said that if we commit our ground forces in Korea we cannot at the same time carry out our other commitments without mobilization. He wondered if it was better to wait now on the question of mobilization of the National Guard. He thought it would be preferable to wait a few days.

THE PRESIDENT said he wished the Joint Chiefs to think about this and to let him know in a few days time. He said "I don't want to go to war".

GENERAL COLLINS stated that if we were going to commit ground forces in Korea we must mobilize.

MR. ACHESON suggested that we should hold mobilization in reserve.

MR. JOHNSON said he hoped these steps already authorized will settle the Korean question.

THE PRESIDENT said the next question would be the mobilization of the Fleet Reserve.

ADMIRAL SHERMAN said there must be a degree of balance.

THE PRESIDENT noted that there is some pretty good air in the National Guard. He had never been in favor of this and thought it should be like the Naval Reserve.

GENERAL VANDENBERG said he was very glad to hear the President say this.

ADMIRAL SHERMAN asked whether MacArthur could anchor the fleet in Formosan ports if necessary.

THE PRESIDENT asked Mr. Acheson what he thought about this.

MR. ACHESON

---

MR. ACHESON said that they should go ahead and do it.

ADMIRAL SHERMAN said this would be the best procedure.

GENERAL COLLINS remarked that if we had had standing orders we could have stopped this. We must consider this problem for the future.

THE PRESIDENT said he agreed.

MR. JOHNSON said that if there was danger of a Russian veto in the Security Council the President's statement should be put out before the Security Council meets tomorrow.

MR. ACHESON agreed.

S/A:PC:Jessup:mtb

## Supporting Question 2

Source C: Oral history interview with Richard Hilton for the Korean War Legacy Project.

https://koreanwarlegacy.org/interviews/richard-arthur-christopher-rich-hilton

USED WITH PERMISSION FROM THE KOREAN WAR LEGACY PROJECT

Richard Arthur Christopher ("Rich") Hilton was born on May 2, 1933 in Roslyn (Long Island), New York. During the Korean War, Mr. Hilton worked on missile technology due to his proficiency with mathematics. His work with missiles saw him stationed in Albuquerque and White Sands, New Mexico. After his service, Mr. Hilton suffered numerous injuries in a car wreck, which left him blind, without a sense of smell, but proud of his time in the Army, even though he lacks many memories of his time in the service.

## Supporting Question 2

Source D: Oral history interview with Earl A. House for the Korean War Legacy Project.

https://koreanwarlegacy.org/interviews/earl-a-house

USED WITH PERMISSION FROM THE KOREAN WAR LEGACY PROJECT

Earl A. House was born in Baltimore, Maryland, on August 30, 1931. After leaving high school early and enlisting in the naval reserves, Mr. House decided to enlist in the Army full time at the beginning of the Korean War. After he completed basic training, Mr. House was sent to Korea. The reality of war quickly subdued his initial excitement for fighting in the war. After receiving a shoulder injury, Mr. House drove a truck and jeep that transported military personnel. He sees his service as having contributed to stopping the spread of communism.

# Supporting Question 2

FEATURED SOURCE Source E: Excerpts from a summary by the United Nations Command [UNC] in Korea, examining the role of the United States in involving the UN in the Korean War, United States Forces Korea website.

http://www.usfk.mil/About/United-Nations-Command

The predawn quiet of a rainy, peaceful Sunday morning, June 25, 1950, was abruptly shattered by the crash of cannons and the snarl of automatic weapons as soldiers of North Korea marched southward....

Two days later, the United Nations called on the countries of the world to unite and assist in driving the invader from the ROK [Republic of Korea]. In its resolution, the UN Security Council named the United States as executive agent to implement the resolution and direct UN military operations in Korea.

President Harry S. Truman, armed with the UN resolution and recognizing a threat to the free world, determined the U.S. could no longer remain neutral while communist powers trampled the free nations of the world.

Douglas MacArthur, [General of the Army and Commander-in-Chief of the] Far East Command, was ordered to provide whatever assistance was needed to repel this invasion. General MacArthur committed U.S. air and naval forces and on July 24, in Tokyo, established General Headquarters, United Nations Command.

## UNITED NATIONS APPEAL

By then, the UN had issued a further appeal to all member nations to provide what military and other aid they could to assist the ROK Government in repelling the invaders. The first ground troops to enter battle on the side of the ROK were advance elements of the U.S. 21st Infantry Regiment, 24th Infantry Division. Units were airlifted from occupation duties in Japan to form "Task Force Smith." The unit was committed on July 5th a few miles north of Osan.

In the face of overpowering enemy strength, the UNC fought delaying actions as ROK and U.S. units withdrew down the peninsula. Outnumbered and out-gunned, they traded space for time as they waited for the pledged assistance from other countries of the UN.

On August 29, 1950, the British Commonwealth's 27th Brigade arrived at Pusan to join the UNC, which until then included only ROK and U.S. forces. The 27th Brigade moved into the Naktong River line west of Taegu.

Troop units from other countries of the UN followed in rapid succession; Australia, Belgium, Canada, Colombia, Ethiopia, France, Greece, Luxembourg, the Netherlands, New Zealand, the Philippines, Thailand and Turkey. The Union of South Africa provided air units which fought alongside the air forces of other member nations. Denmark, India, Norway, and Sweden provided medical units. Italy provided a hospital, even though it was not a UN member.

## KEEP THE FREE WORLD FREE

[...]

On July 27, 1953, the shooting ended. An armistice was signed at Panmunjom which provided for the end of the fighting and eventual political settlement of the war. The shooting ended, but the troops remained, each side pulling back 2,000 meters from the last line of military contact to insure peace, to watch the Demilitarized Zone, and to guard against any resumption of hostilities.

**THE PRICE OF FREEDOM**

In a green field at Tanggok, located near the port of Pusan, stand myriad reminders of the Korean War. Simple white crosses, standing near the sign of the "Crescent and the Star" and the "Star of David" are bleak, symbolic representatives of the 33,629 Americans, numberless Koreans, 717 Turkish soldiers, and 1,109 soldiers of the United Kingdom who gave their lives during the struggle. Also sharing this place of honor are the symbols for the dead of the 12 other nations whose fighting men died to keep Korea free.

With the coming of the armistice, UNC members turned their attention to the tremendous task of assisting in rebuilding a war-torn economy. Assisting the people of the ROK in restoring and reconstructing a nation almost completely devastated by a war that leveled cities and destroyed farmlands was a gigantic project that was years in the accomplishment.

**TROOP STRENGTHS**

Peak strength for the UNC was 932,964 on July 27, 1953—the day the Armistice Agreement was signed:

- Republic of Korea: 590,911
- Colombia: 1,068
- United States: 302,483
- Belgium: 900
- United Kingdom: 14,198
- South Africa: 826
- Canada: 6,146
- The Netherlands: 819
- Turkey: 5,453

- Luxembourg: 44
- Australia: 2,282
- Philippines: 1,496
- New Zealand: 1,385
- Thailand: 1,204
- Ethiopia: 1,271
- Greece: 1,263
- France: 1,119

# Supporting Question 2

FEATURED SOURCE Source F: Note by the White House Staff Secretary, L. Arthur Minnich, about President Dwight D. Eisenhower's policy towards Korea after the armistice, January 5, 1954.

http://eisenhower.archives.gov

At the Bipartisan Conference on January 5, 1954, the President made a clear statement of American policy toward Korea, which amounted to a complete backing of the policies announced in recent weeks by himself and [Secretary of State John Foster] Dulles. He pointed out that the recent announcement in regard to inability to confine hostilities to Korea should the fighting be renewed, was in no sense a criticism of past Administrations but rather a recognition of the new situation which now obtains. He said that the Administration believed, speaking generally, in the doctrine of hot pursuit--that is, of using our full strength to destroy bases used against us. He commented that we cannot allow Communist intransigence to keep us deployed too widely.

He indicated that the decision to withdraw divisions from Korea was based on a unanimous JCS [Joint Chiefs of Staff] decision, and he pointed out that the accomplishment of training of Koreans will result in maintenance of total ground strength at the maximum levels specified by the armistice.

Later in the meeting, he replied to a question by Rep. Vinson by saying that the withdrawal of divisions would have the effect of showing the Communists that we are confident in the strength of our naval and air arms, and that this will have greater impact than any reliance on ground forces of which they are not afraid. Sec. Dulles reinforced this with comment on the possible Communist desire to pull our troops into Asia where they could not be effective in the face of surplus Chinese manpower. Sec. Dulles also commented that President Rhee will be less apt to break the truce if the possibility of embroiling the United States is eliminated by the withdrawal of troops.

Still later in the discussion the President expressed his feeling that the withdrawal of troops would not have adverse effect on our Allies since we are making clear that we will fight offensively should a new outbreak occur. He concluded by saying that in the long run it might develop, of course, that Rep. Vinson's approach was right and his own was wrong, but that all the indications are that a new approach has to be tried and he stands ready to modify policy should it become necessary to do so.

Minnich
Declassified 11/8/85

# Supporting Question 3

Source A: Mutual Defense Treaty Between the United States and the Republic of Korea, October 1, 1953.

http://www.usfk.mil/Portals/105/Documents/SOFA/H_Mutual%20Defense%20Treaty_1953.pdf

**MUTUAL DEFENSE TREATY BETWEEN THE UNITED STATES AND THE REPUBLIC OF KOREA[1]**

October 1, 1953

The Parties to this Treaty,

Reaffirming their desire to live in peace with all peoples and governments, and desiring to strengthen the fabric of peace in the Pacific area, desiring to declare publicly and formally their common determination to defend themselves against external armed attack so that no potential aggressor could be under the illusion that either of them stands alone in the Pacific area, desiring further to strengthen their efforts for collective defense for the preservation of peace and security pending the development of a more comprehensive and effective system of regional security in the Pacific area, have agreed as follows:

**ARTICLE I**
The Parties undertake to settle any international disputes in which they may be involved by peaceful means in such a manner that international peace and security and justice are not endangered and to refrain in their international relations from the threat or use of force in any manner inconsistent with the Purposes of the United Nations, or obligations assumed by any Party toward the United Nations.

**ARTICLE II**
The Parties will consult together whenever, in the opinion of either of them, the political independence or security of either of the Parties is threatened by external armed attack. Separately and jointly, by self help and mutual aid, the Parties will maintain and develop appropriate means to deter armed attack and will take suitable measures in consultation and agreement to implement this Treaty and to further its purposes.

**ARTICLE III**
Each Party recognizes that an armed attack in the Pacific area on either of the Parties in territories now under their respective administrative control, or hereafter recognized by one of the Parties as lawfully brought under the administrative control of the other, would be dangerous to its own peace and safety and declares that it would act to meet the common danger in accordance with its constitutional processes.

**ARTICLE IV**
The Republic of Korea grants, and the United States of America accepts, the right to dispose United States land, air and sea forces in and about the territory of the Republic of Korea as determined by mutual agreement.

**ARTICLE V**
This Treaty shall be ratified by the United States of America and the Republic of Korea in accordance with their respective constitutional processes and will come into force when instruments of ratification thereof have been exchanged by them at Washington.[2]

**ARTICLE VI**
This Treaty shall remain in force indefinitely. Either Party may terminate it one year after notice has been given to the other Party.

IN WITNESS WHEREOF the undersigned Plenipotentiaries have signed this Treaty.

DONE in duplicate at Washington, in the English and Korean languages, this first day of October 1953.

## UNDERSTANDING OF THE UNITED STATES[3]

[The United States Senate gave its advice and consent to the ratification of the treaty subject to the following understanding:]

It is the understanding of the United States that neither party is obligated, under Article III of the above Treaty, to come to the aid of the other except in case of an external armed attack against such party; nor shall anything in the present Treaty be construed as requiring the United States to give assistance to Korea except in the event of an armed attack against territory which has been recognized by the United States as lawfully brought under the administrative control of the Republic of Korea.

[The United States communicated the text of the understanding to the Republic of Korea in a note of January 28, 1954, acknowledged by the Republic of Korea in a note of February 1, 1954. The text of the understanding was included in the President's proclamation of November 17, 1954.]

1.  TIAS 3097, 5 UST 23602376. Ratification advised by the Senate Jan. 26, 1954, and ratified by the President Feb. 5, 1954, subject to an understanding; entered into force Nov. 17, 1954.

2.  Ratifications were exchanged Nov. 17, 1954.

3.  TIAS 3097.

*AMERICAN FOREIGN POLICY 1950-1955, BASIC DOCUMENTS,* VOLUMES I AND II, DEPARTMENT OF STATE PUBLICATION 6446, GENERAL FOREIGN POLICY SERIES 117, WASHINGTON, DC: U.S. GOVERNMENT PRINTING OFFICE, 1957

# Supporting Question 3

**FEATURED SOURCE**      Source B: Oral history interview with George H. Campbell for the Korean War Legacy Project.

**https://koreanwarlegacy.org/interviews/george-h-campbell**

USED WITH PERMISSION FROM THE KOREAN WAR LEGACY PROJECT

George H. Campbell enlisted in the Army in 1951 in hopes that he would have more say in his military career than he would have if he had been drafted. After attending the University of Florida for two years, Campbell used medical training he received to become a medical airman in the U.S. Army. Although he was not stationed in Korea during the war, Mr. Campbell became a medical equipment inspector and lived in Korea (Busan) with his family for three years in the early 1970s. He looks back at his work as providing a form of support to the Republic of Korea.

## Supporting Question 3

FEATURED SOURCE Source C: Oral history interview with Charles Rangel for the Korean War Legacy Project.

https://koreanwarlegacy.org/interviews/congressman-charles-rangel

USED WITH PERMISSION FROM THE KOREAN WAR LEGACY PROJECT

Charles Rangel was born on June 11, 1930 in Harlem, New York. At the age of 17, he enlisted in the military as a way to help support his family. During the Korean War, Mr. Rangel served in the 2nd Infantry Division. He was awarded the Bronze Star and Purple Heart for leading a group of men out of a Chinese encirclement at Kunu Ri. He has famously noted that being injured that day was the worst day of his life, and that he has "never had a bad day since." Rangel is best known for his post-military career as a U.S. Congressional Representative for the state of New York (1971-2017).

This interview is also a source used in Chapter 4 of this book.

## Supporting Question 3

FEATURED SOURCE Source D: Choe Sang-Hun, "Allies for 67 Years, U.S. and South Korea Split Over North Korea," *The New York Times*, September 4, 2017 (excerpt).

https://www.nytimes.com/2017/09/04/world/asia/north-korea-nuclear-south-us-alliance.html

"'South Korea is finding, as I have told them, that their talk of appeasement with North Korea will not work, they only understand one thing!' Mr. Trump said on Twitter. The tone of Mr. Trump's statements stunned officials here [in Seoul, South Korea] and underscored what unlikely partners he and Mr. Moon are, at a time when their countries' 67-year-old military alliance faces an ever-more-dangerous regime in Pyongyang. Mr. Moon, who was elected in May promising to seek dialogue with North Korea, fired back at Mr. Trump, insisting that the crisis be resolved peacefully."

# How Should We **Talk with North Korea**?

Thomas Clouse, Grant Stringer, and Kathy Swan

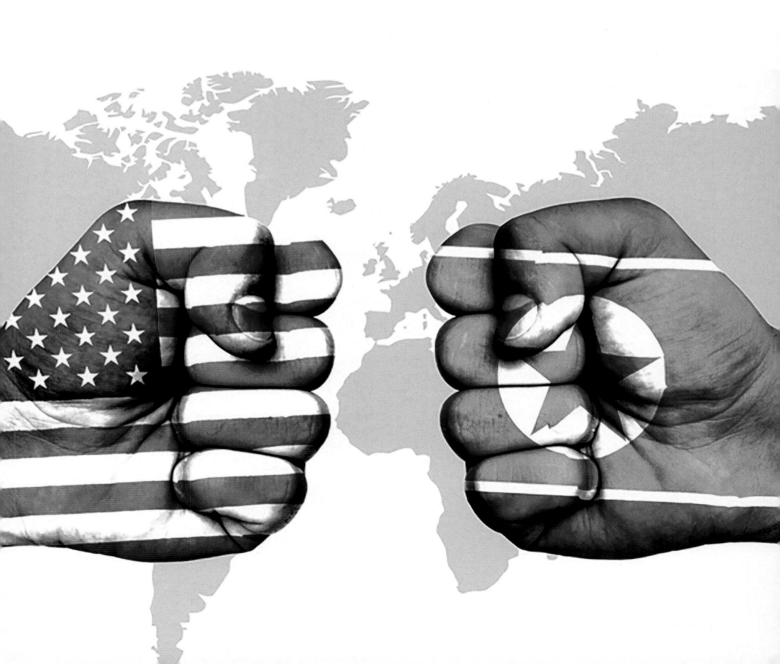

# HOW SHOULD WE TALK WITH NORTH KOREA?

| C3 Framework Indicator | **D2.Civ.6.9-12**. Critique relationships among governments, civil societies, and economic markets. |
|---|---|
| **Staging the Compelling Question** | Analyze a series of political cartoons about the relationship between the United States and North Korea to make inferences about tensions in the relationship. |

| SUPPORTING QUESTION 1 | SUPPORTING QUESTION 2 | SUPPORTING QUESTION 3 |
|---|---|---|
| How has the United States talked with North Korea? | What are the advantages and disadvantages of how the United States talks with North Korea? | How is the United States talking with North Korea right now? (Research Opportunity) |
| **FORMATIVE PERFORMANCE TASK** | **FORMATIVE PERFORMANCE TASK** | **FORMATIVE PERFORMANCE TASK** |
| List the approaches used by the United States when talking with North Korea and provide examples of each. | Create a graphic organizer that lists both benefits and drawbacks to the approaches of talking with North Korea. | Update the graphic organizer by adding benefits and drawbacks to how the United States is talking with North Korea right now. |
| **FEATURED SOURCES** | **FEATURED SOURCES** | **FEATURED SOURCES** |
| **Source A:** Article by Priyanka Boghani, "The U.S. and North Korea on the Brink: A Timeline," PBS Frontline, June 12, 2018<br>**Source B:** Article by Arshad Mohammed and Matt Spetalnick, "U.S. Pursues Direct Diplomacy with North Korea Despite Trump Rejection," Reuters, October 31, 2017<br>**Source C:** Tweets from President Donald Trump about North Korea, January 2, 2018<br>**Source D:** Article from Al Jazeera, with an accompanying video, "Inside Story: Are U.S. and North Korea on the verge of nuclear war?" | **Source A:** Article by Michael E. O'Hanlon, "Americans Have Military Options for North Korea (but They're All Bad)," *National Interest*, January 4, 2018<br>**Source B:** Excerpt from a 2017 article by Jenny Town, "Mitigating the Nuclear Threat on the Korean Peninsula."<br>**Source C:** Video debate between former ambassadors and nuclear negotiators Robert L. Gallucci and Christopher Hill, hosted by and held at the Asia Society, March 22, 2018 | Sources will vary. |

| | ARGUMENT How should we talk with North Korea? Construct a claim and a counterclaim that address the compelling question using evidence. |
|---|---|
| **Summative Performance Task** | |
| | EXTENSION Have an informed conversation with an adult about how we should talk with North Korea. |

# Overview
## Inquiry Description

The compelling questions for this inquiry call on students to research the history of diplomatic relations between the United States and North Korea. How to talk with North Korea has been an important diplomatic question for U.S. presidents from Truman to Trump. At times that question has been answered with the use of direct diplomacy with North Korea, and at other times with the use of indirect diplomacy—compelling other countries to impose sanctions and other punitive measures on North Korea. At the present time, Kim Jong-un, the current leader of North Korea, has pushed forward on nuclear armament at a much faster pace than his predecessors, fueled by worsening political relations with the international community. Additionally, despite assertions that North Korea would have to choose between its pursuit of nuclear weapons and its economic development, the North Korean economy has continued to grow amid worsening sanctions and waning international trade. These developments have brought the relationship between the United States and North Korea to the forefront of international relations. Students will attempt to understand how the United States has talked—and is talking—with North Korea, weighing the benefits and drawbacks of each approach to answer the question, "How should the United States talk with North Korea, and why is it important in the resolution of North Korean issues?"

This inquiry is expected to take three to five 50-minute class periods. The inquiry time frame could expand if teachers think their students need additional instructional experiences (i.e., supporting questions, formative performance tasks, and featured sources). Inquiries are not scripts, so teachers are encouraged to modify and adapt them in order to meet the needs and interests of their particular students. Resources can also be modified as necessary to meet individualized education programs (IEPs) or Section 504 plans for students with disabilities.

## Structure of the Inquiry

In addressing the compelling question "How should the United States talk with North Korea?" students will work through supporting questions, a performance task, and a number of sources in order to construct a claim and counterclaim with evidence.

### STAGING THE COMPELLING QUESTION

The focused inquiry opens with students analyzing a series of political cartoons that parody the relationship between U.S. President Donald Trump and Kim Jong-un of North Korea. In analyzing the sources, students will make inferences about the state of diplomatic relations between the two leaders, and what the impact of that relationship might be. Teachers may want students to analyze the political cartoons by using the National Archives' political cartoon analysis worksheet at:

https://www.archives.gov/files/education/lessons/worksheets/cartoon_analysis_worksheet_former.pdf

## SUPPORTING QUESTION 1

The first supporting question is "How has the United States talked with North Korea?" It helps students build content knowledge by having them review the different ways in which the United States has attempted to talk with (or about) North Korea. The formative performance task calls on students to list the different approaches used by the United States when talking with North Korea, and give an example of each. Featured Source A is an article from PBS Frontline that has students examine the different tactics the U.S. government has used to talk with North Korea since the ceasefire in the Korean War. Source B is a Reuters article that explores how the United States is still pursuing a diplomatic relationship with North Korea, even as President Trump is taking a hardline stance through social media. Source C consists of two tweets that President Trump sent on January 2, 2018. The first discussues a meeting between North and South Korea, while the second attacks North Korea for its testing of Intercontinental Ballistic Missiles (ICBMs), with Trump alluding to the superiority of the United States' nuclear arsenal. Teachers may want to point out that the president sent the tweets under his @realDonaldTrump twitter handle and not the official presidential account, @POTUS. Source D is an Al Jazeera article that discusses the ways in which the United States, especially President Trump, talks to and about North Korea, and how those linguistic choices are interpreted by North Koreans and others.

## SUPPORTING QUESTION 2

Building from the first supporting question, the second supporting question—"What are the advantages and disadvantages of how the United States talks with Korea?"—has students create a graphic organizer that lists possible benefits and drawbacks to the different approaches the United States has used in talking with North Korea. Ultimately, students will have to weigh those benefits and drawbacks when answering the compelling question. Featured Source A is an op-ed piece by Michael E. O'Hanlon, Senior Fellow for Foreign Policy at the Brookings Institution. O'Hanlon discusses the pros and cons of potential military options against North Korea and why none are likely to solve the problem. Featured Source B is an article by Jenny Town, Fellow of the Stimson Center, examining the range of U.S options for mitigating the nuclear threat on the Korean Peninsula. Source C is a video debate, hosted by the Asia Society, between former ambassadors and nuclear negotiators Robert L. Gallucci and Christopher Hill, in which they discuss their experiences and lessons learned while negotiating with North Korea.

## SUPPORTING QUESTION 3

The third supporting question—"How is the United States talking with North Korea right now?"—asks students to research current articles that detail the way the United States currently engages with North Korea. Students will use information from relevant articles to add to their graphic organizer and strengthen their argument before answering the compelling question. The need for a third supporting question in this inquiry is due to the volatile nature of the relationship between the United States and North Korea, in which the two countries vacillate between the brink of war and civil diplomacy with disconcerting frequency. Thus, the third supporting question focuses on examining the way the relationship is changing in as close to real time as possible. Sources are not provided in this chapter and will vary depending on the time at which students do their research, but teachers will want to encourage students to evaluate each source with respect to credibility and bias.

## SUMMATIVE PERFORMANCE TASK

In the summative performace task, students construct an evidence-based argument responding to the prompt, "How should the United States talk with North Korea?" Teachers will want to have students focus their responses by referring to the graphic organizers they created for this inquiry. In this focused inquiry, students are asked to develop a claim and counterclaim supported by evidence they examined during the inquiry. Students' arguments will vary, but could include any of the following:

- The United States should take a strong stance when talking with North Korea. Diplomatic relations with the country have been difficult for many years, and with North Korea developing nuclear capabilities, the stakes are extremely high.

- The United States should take a strong stance when talking with North Korea. Although war would not be ideal, the threat of North Korea's growing nuclear capabilities is too great a risk to the United States, our partners in Asia (including South Korea), and to the world.

- The United States should take a strong stance when talking with North Korea, but must use the appropriate channels for defining that stance—not Twitter statements by the President.

- The United States should take a diplomatic stance when talking with Korea, because diplomacy represents the wishes of our partners in the region, including South Korea and Japan, and is promoted also by China and Russia.

- The United States should take a diplomatic stance when talking with Korea. While diplomatic relations have fallen through in the past, an invasion of North Korea could have negative consequences for U.S. relations in the region and for our allies, such as South Korea and Japan.

- The United States should not talk with North Korea, but instead focus on talking with other countries, especially China, to put sanctions and other punitive measures on North Korea for its continued pursuit of a nuclear weapons program.

Students could extend these arguments by having an informed conversation about how the United States should talk with North Korea.

## Staging the Compelling Question

**FEATURED SOURCE** Michael Cavna, collection of political cartoons depicting the current relationship between the United States and North Korea, *The Washington Post*, compiled August, 9, 2017.

https://www.washingtonpost.com/news/comic-riffs/wp/2017/08/09/how-trump-and-north-korea-are-skewered-with-satires-fire-and-fury-according-to-cartoons/?utm_term=.7c002d344cc4

BY EMAD HAJJAJ/JORDAN (CAGLECARTOONS.COM) 2017. REPRODUCED BY PERMISSION OF CAGLE CARTOONS, INC.

BY PAT BAGLEY/ *SALT LAKE TRIBUNE* (CAGLECARTOONS.COM) 2017. REPRODUCED BY PERMISSION OF CAGLE CARTOONS, INC.

NEXT BREAKTHROUGH in NORTH KOREA'S NUCLEAR MINIATURIZATION...?

BY NATE BEELER/
*COLUMBUS DISPATCH*
(CAGLECARTOONS.COM)
2017. REPRODUCED BY
PERMISSION OF CAGLE
CARTOONS, INC.

## Supporting Question

**FEATURED SOURCE**    Source A: Article by Priyanka Boghani, "The U.S. and North Korea on the Brink: A Timeline," PBS Frontline, June 12, 2018.

*For the text of this article, see Chapter 11, pages 134–139.*

## Supporting Question

**FEATURED SOURCE**    Source B: Article by Arshad Mohammed and Matt Spetalnick, "U.S. Pursues Direct Diplomacy with North Korea Despite Trump Rejection," Reuters, October 31, 2017.

https://www.reuters.com/article/us-northkorea-missiles-usa-exclusive/exclusive-u-s-pursues-direct-diplomacy-with-north-korea-despite-trump-rejection-idUSKBN1D136I

Using the so-called "New York channel," Joseph Yun, U.S. negotiator with North Korea, has been in contact with diplomats at Pyongyang's United Nations mission, the official said, at a time when an exchange of bellicose insults between Trump and North Korean leader Kim Jong Un has fueled fears of military conflict.

While U.S. Secretary of State Rex Tillerson on October 17 said he would continue "diplomatic efforts ... until the first bomb drops," the official's comments were the clearest sign the United States was directly discussing issues beyond the release of American prisoners, despite Trump having dismissed direct talks as pointless.

**FEATURED SOURCE**    Source C: Tweets from President Donald Trump about North Korea, January 2, 2018.

https://twitter.com/realDonaldTrump

**Donald J. Trump** ✔
@realDonaldTrump

Sanctions and "other" pressures are beginning to have a big impact on North Korea. Soldiers are dangerously fleeing to South Korea. Rocket man now wants to talk to South Korea for first time. Perhaps that is good news, perhaps not - we will see!

6:08 AM - 2 Jan 2018

**Donald J. Trump** ✔
@realDonaldTrump

North Korean Leader Kim Jong Un just stated that the "Nuclear Button is on his desk at all times." Will someone from his depleted and food starved regime please inform him that I too have a Nuclear Button, but it is a much bigger & more powerful one than his, and my Button works!

7:49 PM - 2 Jan 2018

## Supporting Question 1

**FEATURED SOURCE**

Source D: Article from Al Jazeera, with an accompanying video, "Inside Story: Are U.S. and North Korea on the verge of nuclear war?" The article is "North Korea: U.S. Planning a 'Bloody Nose' First Strike," Al Jazeera, February 6, 2018. The unknown author of the article discusses the ways in which the United States talks to and about North Korea, and the effect of those choices.

https://www.aljazeera.com/news/2018/02/north-korea-planning-bloody-nose-strike-180206210238738.html

A "bloody nose" attack refers to a limited military strike against the North's nuclear weapons sites that allegedly would not result in large-scale death and destruction.

The *Rodong Sinmun*, the North's ruling party newspaper, said on Tuesday that U.S. criticism of Pyongyang's weapons programmes and its human rights record was setting the stage for an attack.

*The video is embedded at the end of the article. The video is titled, "Inside Story: Are U.S. and North Korea on the verge of nuclear war?" The clip runs for the first 03:54 of the show.*

## Supporting Question 2

**FEATURED SOURCE**

Source A: Article by Michael E. O'Hanlon discussing the pros and cons of potential military options against North Korea, "America Has Military Options for North Korea (but They're All Bad)," *National Interest*, January 4, 2018.

http://nationalinterest.org/feature/america-has-military-options-north-korea-theyre-all-bad-23940

Is the Trump administration considering preventive military action of some sort against the North Korean regime of Kim Jong-un? With various U.S. officials saying that "time is running out" for a diplomatic solution to the nuclear and missile standoff with the DPRK [Democratic People's Republic of Korea], that may be the case—or at least the intended message.

A review of the plausible military options available to the United States underscores two central points. First, the Trump administration is not alone in thinking about them. Previous U.S. administrations, including Democratic ones, have done so, too. Second, however, none of those options really hold water. The risks of escalation are not worth the potential benefits. Consider these options:

### Shoot Down Long-Range Missile Launches

One military option would be to prevent North Korea from completing any more long-range missile tests to perfect ICBM [Intercontinental Ballistic Missile] technology. This idea was proposed in 2006 by two Democratic secretaries of defense, William Perry and Ashton Carter. The missiles could be destroyed by precision munitions launched from aircraft just before launch. Or they could be shot down in flight by a U.S. missile defense system; based on previous testing, any such shot might have a 25 to 75 percent chance of success.

However, in response, North Korea might accelerate its development of solid-fueled ICBMs, which have a launch preparation process that is difficult to detect. The United States might not shoot down such ICBMs effectively in peacetime or in war. North Korea might also request permission from China or Russia to launch test ICBMs northward or westward rather than eastward, which means the missiles would land in Siberia or the Gobi Desert (or even the Arctic Ocean).

Furthermore, this idea does not address North Korea's growing inventory of perhaps several dozen nuclear warheads (and shorter-range missiles that could carry them) that already put Seoul and Tokyo at risk, including the hundreds of thousands of Americans living there.

**Blockade North Korean Ports**
To the credit of the Trump administration, the UN Security Council has just imposed additional sanctions on the DPRK. These would, among other things, reduce certain types of fuel imports up to 90 percent and severely squeeze the remittances sent home by North Korean workers living in places like Russia.

A blockade by the United States and allied navies could seem a logical way to ensure that such sanctions were actually respected. Of course, a military blockade is, by standard international law, an act of war. Enforcing it could require the use of lethal ordnance against any North Korean or other ships that refused to allow boarding and inspection. In response to such a blockade, North Korea could be expected, at a minimum, to shoot at any nearby ships that were targeting its own vessels, risking American casualties.

Even more importantly, this option would not curtail trade across North Korean land borders or airspace. Thus, it would neither reduce the existing threat posed by North Korea, nor likely slow further growth of nuclear and missile arsenals in the future. It would tighten the economic squeeze, but fail to reduce the military threat.

**Destroy North Korean Nuclear Infrastructure**
Just as Israel preemptively attacked Iraqi and Syrian nuclear reactors in 1981 and 2007, the United States and/or South Korea could take aim at parts of North Korea's nuclear infrastructure, most likely with stealthy attack aircraft. Specifically, the nuclear reactor that is under construction but not yet operational could be destroyed without dispersal of highly radioactive material, as could the uranium centrifuge complex at that same site.

Unfortunately, such preventive strikes could not eliminate any second uranium enrichment facility that North Korea may have built at an unknown site. Nor could they humanely destroy the operational research reactor that has produced all of North Korea's plutonium to date. An attack on such a site would create a miniature Chernobyl or Fukushima-like outcome, lethally spreading highly radioactive reactor waste over an area of hundreds of square miles downwind. Such an attack would be unlikely to reach any of the several dozen warheads North Korea already likely possesses, since U.S. officials do not know where they are located.

**Target Kim Jong-un Directly**
Like the start of Operation Iraqi Freedom in 2003, when the Bush administration attempted to kill Saddam Hussein in an early "shock and awe" strike, the United States and South Korea could target Kim Jong-un. U.S. law prohibits assassinating foreign political leaders.

But if Kim were declared the military commander of a nation still technically at war with the United Nations and in violation of its cease-fire obligations (due to frequent repeated aggressions against South Korea over the years), this issue might be finessed, at least legalistically.

However, the United States might miss Kim Jong-un in any such attempt, as the 2003 Iraqi case demonstrates. Whether successful or not, North Korea might respond with similar attempts against western leaders.

And where would even a successful operation get the United States? Unless U.S. officials were able to message virtually all other senior North Korean leaders in advance, and persuade them to accept amnesty and exile if they chose not to resist, killing Kim Jong-un might just lead to the replacement of one extremist leader with another. North Korean military command and control might also splinter, with some elements opting for a violent response against the United States and ROK [the Republic of Korea—the official name for South Korea] rather than for surrender.

In short, whatever their individual appeal, each of these options would appear to promise only mediocre effects against the North Korean threats that matter most to the United States. Let us hope the Trump administration understands as much, and that it is using its threats of military action to create a sense of urgency about the need for North Korean concessions rather than to signal looming attack.

*Michael O'Hanlon is a senior fellow and director of research at the Brookings Institution's Foreign Policy Program.*

## Supporting Question 2

**FEATURED SOURCE**    Source B: Excerpt from an article by Jenny Town, Fellow of the Stimson Center, "Mitigating the Nuclear Threat on the Korean Peninsula," which was written in 2017 for the web resource TeachingAboutNorthKorea.org.

Since 2002, efforts to curtail North Korea's pursuit of nuclear weapons have been largely focused on economic sanctions to try to "raise the cost" for the North's nuclear ambitions high enough to convince Pyongyang to abandon this path. However, it has become evident, especially in recent years, that implementation of such sanctions has been incomplete and unable to stop procurement channels. Moreover, despite the negative impact these sanctions have on the North's potential economic development, Pyongyang has clearly decided this is a cost it is willing to pay.

Although North Korea often claims that its nuclear deterrent helps "keep peace" in the region by staving off U.S. military intervention, the opposite is now true. The United States and international community have always been opposed to North Korea developing nuclear weapons, but the combination of the North's recent advancements in weapons technology, its unrelenting pace of nuclear and missile testing, and its dramatic and hostile rhetoric have led the U.S. government and a growing faction within the Washington policy community to the conclusion that it's now "time to get tough" on North Korea. What "tough" actually means is still amorphous, but generally falls back on old policy tools including harsher economic sanctions against North Korea, cutting into commercial sectors believed to be raising funds for the North's Weapons of Mass Destruction (WMD) programs; cracking down on companies and individuals in other countries known to have worked with North Korean designated entities; and imposing tighter controls on banking systems, cutting off Pyongyang's access to dollar-based business transactions and raising the reputational risk of doing business with North Korea.

These coercive measures are certainly not new or unique to the Trump administration. Under the Obama administration, the rationale for increasing these coercive measures was to "sharpen" Pyongyang's choice between economic prosperity and WMD development. The premise was that North Korea could not pursue both; the hope being, of course, that they would prioritize potential economic performance over a seemingly unnecessary nuclear capability.

In general, the United States has five categories of policy options: (1) continue the status quo, and try to contain the escalation; (2) acquiesce to a North Korea with nuclear weapons; (3) delegate the problem to other actors; (4) negotiate to try to achieve a denuclearized Korean peninsula; or (5) take military actions.

When it comes to acquiescence, there are political reasons, including fear of undermining the nonproliferation regime, that prevent the United States from formally recognizing North Korea as a nuclear-armed state. But there are domestic reasons now as well. Experts have been warning of the North's technological advancements for years, but the threat it posed for most Americans, including policymakers, was still largely existential. Unlike our allies in the region—South Korea and Japan—who have lived under a real threat from Pyongyang for decades, Americans have had the luxury of being "out of range" and thus, this issue was largely out of mind. However, the successful flight tests of a North Korean inter-continental ballistic missile (the Hwasong-14) in July 2017 forced Americans to internalize the North Korean threat as something real and worrisome; fueled by sensationalist media coverage and a general lack of knowledge about North Korea, the North Korean ICBM created a sense of panic among the public. People all across the country were suddenly afraid North Korea would attack, unprovoked, at any minute, especially as Trump began to threaten back. So while in the past, the North Korea's pursuit of nuclear weapons may have been seen as more of a nuisance to most Americans, the threat perception is now high. North Korea has successfully captured the American imagination with active threats (albeit in a retaliatory effort) to use nuclear weapons against the U.S. The U.S. government has never been willing to politically recognize North Korea as a nuclear-armed state, but American public opinion now means that acquiescence is even less politically feasible.

When it comes to delegation, the U.S. strategy, especially under the Obama administration and the beginning of the Trump administration, has been to push responsibility for this problem onto China. There is a prevailing belief that China's economic influence over North Korea provides substantial enough leverage to force Pyongyang back to the negotiating table. However, as we have seen over the past eight years, there are fundamental flaws to this approach.

First, China and the United States have different national security interests that are unlikely to fully align on desired approaches or outcomes on this issue. Second, the idea that leveraging economic influence will, for sure, elicit a specific response from North Korea is a false assumption. Furthermore, given the North's adaptability to sanctions in the past, although they may struggle under the weight of increased economic pressures, they will likely find ways to survive.

Most importantly though, even if China could bring North Korea to the table, the question is: to the table with whom? Without the U.S. being willing to negotiate with North Korea directly or in a multilateral forum, Chinese efforts to coerce North Korea back to talks ring rather hollow. After all, the United States is Pyongyang's main adversary, not China, and the idea that China could broker a deal on America's behalf that guaranteed certain U.S. actions and policies, is simply not credible.

While there is wide agreement in the United States and among our allies, as well as among regional actors, that there are "no good military options" in this situation, there is a growing belief that there are no good negotiating options either. Although North Korea has posed negotiations to the U.S. in the past (through state media) and still continues to frame its stance as not being willing to negotiate on nuclear issues "unless the U.S. hostile policy is removed" (which suggests that there is still a formula in which nuclear issues can be negotiated), the gestures have been lost in a sea of propaganda and brinkmanship and in the unrelenting stream of missile tests. More and more, experts and officials both inside and outside of the U.S. government are interpreting these actions as "Kim Jong Un not being willing to negotiate."

With each new test and more advanced missile type, a growing segment of pundits posit that it is already too late for negotiations—believing North Korea is too far along in its program to be ever willing to reverse course. Furthermore, there is a general tendency to oversimplify the diplomatic track record with North Korea, seeing only the current state of North Korea's WMD program as testament to how futile negotiating with North Korea is, rather than understanding the nuanced successes and failures within that long diplomatic history.

We can see this debate over whether negotiations are even worth trying played out in the White House. Trump's tweet of August 30, 2017 about how "talking is not the answer!", however simplistic, reflects a strong conservative narrative that has become ever more resolute in the belief that any negotiation with North Korea would just appease the North Koreans, but get nothing in return. Secretary of Defense Mattis' contradictory follow-up statement, though, that there are no good military options and that we must find diplomatic solutions, illustrates both the divisive thinking on this issue and the mixed messaging of the U.S. administration.

The U.S. government, having had agreements fall apart quickly after coming to terms both in bilateral and multilateral formats, is reluctant to be humiliated with failure again. Thus, it tends to withhold talks until it sees either concrete signs that North Korea wants to negotiate, such as Pyongyang making unilateral concessionary measures in order to prove its "sincerity," or until the North provides some kind of assurance that success is possible. Consequently, if success cannot be guaranteed, especially within a short amount of time, there is a growing belief that it is not an option worth trying.

However, the North's stepped-up testing, and increasingly confident, aggressive, and hostile posture, has made the status quo no longer tenable either, given the escalatory cycle of provocation and response. The decisions made among the U.S. and its allies to take additional defensive measures against a rising North Korean threat have sparked agitation and retaliatory measures from China and Russia, heightening tensions in the region that are further exacerbated with each new North Korean nuclear and missile test. Doubling down on sanctions without providing diplomatic off-ramps further antagonizes tense relations among the big powers, making cooperation on solving this issue more difficult to achieve.

So far, the U.S. policy of "getting tough" on North Korea has mainly been focused on coercive measures, stemming largely from the belief that negotiations won't work and a reluctance to take military actions. But with each new and more aggressive North Korean WMD test, the sustainability of the status quo diminishes, the political will to try negotiations faces more criticism, and voices advocating military strikes and preventive actions gain more traction. The danger in sharpening choices is that the options may be whittled down to the choice you don't want made. De-escalating the situation is going to take all sides—including North Korea—deciding military choices are not in anyone's best interest, and taking steps to restore options back to the menu before it is too late.

# Supporting Question 2

Source C: Video debate between former ambassadors and nuclear negotiators Robert L. Gallucci and Christopher Hill, moderated by Daniel Russel (Diplomat in Residence and Senior Fellow at the Asia Society Policy Insitute), about the ambassadors' experiences and lessons learned when negotiating with North Korea, "North Korea and the Art of the Deal: Lessons in Hands-On Diplomacy," hosted by and held at the Asia Society, March 22, 2018.

https://asiasociety.org/video/north-korea-and-art-deal-complete

# CONCLUSION

Kathy Swan, John Lee, and S.G. Grant

In these pages, we satisfy two objectives. One is to elevate the curricular potential of Korea and the Korean War for students in elementary, middle, and high school classrooms. The second is to illustrate the power of inquiry as a pedagogical approach, one in which teachers and their students can stretch their intellectual boundaries.

Were this book only a loose collection of lesson plans around Korea and the Korean War, it would still have filled an important role. Korean society writ large and the Korean War in particular are topics well worth students' time and attention. No such collection existed, however, so teachers were left to craft units of study on their own. Some did, most didn't, and Korea remained largely forgotten.

The Korean War Legacy Project (KWLP) has stepped into that void. Under the leadership of Dr. Jongwoo Han, the KWLP is building a compendium of resources that address the needs of both academic scholars and classroom teachers. This book is the maiden effort to support classroom teachers and their students as they engage with a range of topics, issues, and resources around the Korean peninsula, past and present.

The launch of the *College, Career, and Civic Life (C3) Framework for Social Studies State Standards* signaled the importance of the second goal—taking seriously the need to promote a more ambitious approach to teaching and learning.[1] One long-endorsed means of ratcheting up students' learning experiences has been inquiry.[2] Yet, the potential for inquiry-based practice has been dwarfed by the reality of instructional methods rooted in the transmission of knowledge. Of course, content knowledge is important, but so too are a range of disciplinary skills that enable students to maneuver their way through the wealth of ideas and sources that surround them.

One of those skills calls for students to construct and support evidence-based arguments. Learning how to read and interpret sources and how to write descriptions and explanations are important. Yet, these skills reach the height of their usefulness in the development of arguments. Echoing throughout the literature on civic life is the assertion that rational argumentation is the touchstone of public discourse.[3]

While the task of making and supporting arguments is one of the common features of inquiry-based practice, there are others. In order to construct an argument, students need access to a range of disciplinary sources from which they gain the knowledge to make claims and to provide evidence to support those claims. Textbooks can be a source but, as the inquiries in this book demonstrate, students can and should have access to a wide range of information sources. The third component of classroom inquiry—questions—provides the frame. There are lots of ways to engage students in inquiry, but questions, tasks, and sources are the critical components.

The Inquiry Design Model that we developed, and that we and the other authors of chapters in this book have used in the inquiries, privileges these key elements.[4] Compelling and supporting questions, formative and summative performance tasks, and disciplinary sources provide teachers and their students with the elements through which they can explore and examine any worthwhile social studies topic.

And one of those topics is surely the Korean War and its many aftershocks. The elementary, middle, and high school inquiries represented in these pages illustrate how the past and present live together in the ways that people live their everyday lives, in the ways that social, political, and economic institutions operate, and in the diplomatic efforts in which countries engage as they try to resolve pressing issues.

How the Republic of Korea, North Korea, and the United States will navigate their ways into the future remains to be seen. What we know, however, is that every student will be impacted by those efforts. The inquiries in this book cannot prepare them for every eventuality. But they can position even young students in ways that enable them to see clearly and to engage in civic life.

### NOTES

1. National Council for the Social Studies (NCSS), *The College, Career, and Civic Life (C3) Framework for Social Studies State Standards* (Silver Spring, MD: NCSS, 2013).

2. S. G. Grant, K. Swan, and J. Lee, *Inquiry-based Practice in Social Studies Education: The Inquiry Design Model* (New York: Routledge, 2017).

3. M. Edwards, *Civil Society* (Cambridge: Blackwell Publishing, 2004); P. Levine and K. Kawashima-Ginsberg, *Civic Education and Deeper Learning* (Center for Information and Research on Civic Learning and Engagement, January 2015), retrieved from http://jff.org/sites/default/files/publications/materials/Civic-Education-and-Deeper-Learning-012815.pdf; W. Parker, *Teaching Democracy: Unity and Diversity in Public Life* (New York: Teachers College Press, 2003).

4. S. G. Grant, K. Swan, and J. Lee, *Inquiry-based Practice in Social Studies Education: The Inquiry Design Model*, op. cit.; K. Swan, J. Lee, and S. G. Grant, *Inquiry Design Model: Building Inquiries in Social Studies* (Silver Spring: National Council for the Social Studies and C3 Teachers, 2018).

# CONTRIBUTORS

## Authors and Editors

**Kathy Swan** is a professor of social studies education in the College of Education at the University of Kentucky.

**John Lee** is a professor of social studies education in the College of Education at North Carolina State University.

**S.G. Grant** is a professor of social studies education in the Department of Teaching, Learning, and Educational Leadership at Binghamton University.

## Other Authors

**Mona Al-Hayani** is a middle and high school history teacher at Toledo Early College High School in Toledo Public Schools, Ohio.

**Elaine Alvey** is an elementary school teacher who is a doctoral student in education at the University of Georgia.

**Thomas Clouse** is a high school teacher who is a doctoral student in social studies education at the University of Kentucky.

**Carly Muetterties** is a high school teacher who is a doctoral student in social studies education at the University of Kentucky.

**Grant Stringer** is a doctoral student in social studies education at the University of Kentucky and a high school social studies teacher at Scott County High School.